Who Taught You How to Run?

Mike Antoniades

To Joe,

Good luck with the running
& thanks for your support

Mire - A.

ISBN: 978-1-8384475-0-2

FIRST EDITION

www.runningschool.com

This book is intended as a reference only. The information it contains is designed to help you make informed decisions about your running, your fitness, and your health. It is not intended as a substitute for professional medical or fitness advice. As with all exercise programmes, you should consult your doctor before you begin.

Cover Design by Andrea Giorgi
Movement Pattern Graphics by Zoe Baker
Exercise Photographs by The Running School®

DEDICATION

For Thoulla, thank you for putting up with me for the last 43 years, I love you always.

To my Mum, Michelle, Nick and Anna.

THANK YOU

This book would not have been completed without Sheena 'Murphy' All-port. Sheena and I have worked together for 9 years. Over the last few months, she has worked tirelessly on the book, correcting my mistakes, clarifying my thought processes, editing, formatting and generally keeping me on track. Sheena began as a Running School coach but within a few months she did so much more. From coaching to marketing to organising exhibitions and conferences, designing marketing material and logos and writing training manuals. Disagreeing and arguing with me when she thought I was wrong (always very politely!). Along with Nick, my son, she has helped me to grow the Running School. Sheena prefers not to be in the limelight, but she is brilliant at everything she does, including her running. Sheena, thank you for all your help.

It would also not be possible without the help from Nick my son, and all the hard work that he does with the coaching, marketing, and managing our online courses. Which gives me time to coach and teach training courses. Nick is also an exceptional coach and gets a raw deal, as he must also listen to all my ideas and moaning. Thanks Nick.

A big thank you to Suzannah, Harriet, Ruth, Rachel, and Jude for sharing their Running School experiences in the book.

A special thank you to Katie Boyles for her input and insightful editing!

CONTENTS

A Memorable Run

Friday 24th of May 2013 – Hemsbach, Germany 6:45 PM

For the first three to four minutes all you could hear were two sets of footsteps in the forest, the sound bouncing off the dirt track. Then the breathing got heavier and noisier as the two men hit the steep incline of the hill.

"This is really beautiful."

Frank is the tall one breathing out loudly and deliberately, like a whale expelling air out of its blowhole. I am the short one, breathing heavily and trying to pretend I am not struggling to move. "Beautiful and peaceful." I gasp. "Smell that air! Great idea to come running here, Frank."

As we neared the top of the hill, the terrain flattened for a little while and then, as we turned the corner around the bend, the descent begins almost immediately. Another steep one!

"Shit, that hurts! OW! Just ignore me, keep going."

"Do you want to walk?" asked Frank.

"No, you go on and I'll catch up on the next hill."

Frank kept running slowly down the hill, I began to walk gently and then, after a few steps, break into a run again. "Shit, shit, shit" moaning as I slowed down once more. I finally catch him up at the next incline when he starts to slow.

A pattern was beginning to emerge. Frank was faster going down-hill, and I was catching up on the inclines.

"Why do you still run if it hurts so much?" He asked.

"That's a very good question and one Thoulla, my wife, asks me all the time."

It is quiet in the forest, a bit chilly, as it had been raining on and off all day and it was no more than 5 degrees all morning - freezing for the end of May. We are running under the trees. Frank is wearing a heavy sweatshirt, a waterproof top, tracksuit bottoms and a wooly hat. I am in shorts, t-shirt and a windproof top I borrowed off Frank. It's too big for me but this is not a time to be worried about appearances. This was a work trip. I didn't come prepared to run.

Today, I didn't warm-up well. Like most recreational athletes, we warmed-up during the run. A few walks and jogs, a few swings of the arms and butt flicks and we started to run. Not good!

We run around the wide right-hand bend. The sun comes out from beneath the clouds just at the same time. Warm, bright, feeling the heat on the side of our faces. The view from this side is spectacular! The vineyards are just a few meters away to our right. Below you can see all the way down the valley. In the distance, is the city of Manheim. All you can hear up here (besides the heavy breathing) are the birds singing in the late afternoon sunshine.

It's like a scene from the film the 'The Last of the Mohicans.' I can hear the music starting in the background. Running up the path, chasing the deer, leaping from one side of the path to the other. The music is getting louder, the drums stronger, bouncing over a log, getting closer to the deer. He stops. Leaning onto a tree with the left shoulder, getting the rifle ready, bringing the rifle up to the right shoulder. The deer stands still. Listening for strange, unusual sounds, ready to bounce away. The hunter holds his breath, finger on the trigger, squeezes…

"Why do I still run? How long do you have?"

Running in the forest is a breathtaking experience! The glimpses of the sun through the trees. The undulating terrain, up-hill, a flat stretch, then down the hill and up again — make the running tough for two guys who have been

x

sitting down doing presentations all day! Two guys who are not used to running up and down steep hills in a forest! I'm certainly not used to it – I live in London for goodness' sake!

I catch up to Frank at the bottom of the hill doing walking-lunges, trying to catch his breath, waiting for me. He is looking up through the trees, the thick bushes and tall grasses.

Running uphill doesn't hurt as much as it does on the flat and the downhill, where it sends a sharp pain through my knee, because of the osteoarthritis. It ALWAYS hurts in the first twenty minutes anyway, until my body gets warmed up. I never know if I will be able to handle the pain or not until I start running.

So why DO I still run?

It's not because I know that when I sit down later, I will struggle to get up again, as the pain shoots through my knee. I know tomorrow morning, as with most mornings, I will try and put my right foot down and wince in anticipation before the pain hits my knee. I know that it may take the whole day before I am walking without a limp again. I know I won't be able to run again for ten days or so, maybe more. This time, it was three whole weeks. I know that the next time I try to run, I will have to do an exceptionally long warm-up before I know if I *can* run.

"Because Frank... even though it hurts - my knee especially - and even though my back and calves try to compensate all the time to keep me moving and even though my lungs burn and gasp for air until I am really warmed up... **it's because it makes me feel alive!**

Because there is no feeling like it. The feeling of warmth and vitality engulfing your whole body. The clarity it brings to your thoughts. My thoughts!"

How many times have *you* been for a run, even in the middle of the city, after a stressful day at work, starting off with the legs heavy, every move is a struggle, like running through treacle? You really do not want to do this run. You would rather be somewhere else. Then 20 minutes into the run, you come alive, warming up the muscles. You are moving fluently. Weaving in and out of pedestrians, stopping at traffic lights hurrying them up, trying to find a rhythm to help keep you going. Breathing quickly, you feel the sweat on the back of your t-shirt and dripping down your forehead.

Your unconscious mind is working overtime – finding solutions to the day's problems, making a mental to-do list for you to access later. Thoughts of 'What can I eat for dinner?' flow through your conscious mind.

You move your arms faster and put in a burst of speed, when you see a 'proper runner' coming the other way bouncing along, to show that you are not hurting. You focus on correct running technique, trying not to thump the ground when you run, trying to float over the pavement, not drill holes into it.

You begin to feel good, adrenalin is pumping, endorphins are kicking in.

You see a set of stairs leading up to another level and suddenly you start sprinting up the stairs; here comes the music again! The volume building up as you spring up the stairs before you collapse in a heap with jelly legs at the top. YOU are Rocky Balboa! What an unbeatable feeling!

I run because it makes me feel alive!

"Hey Frank, what are you looking at through the trees? Are there deer around here?" I ask.

"Yes, but I'm looking for pigs."

"Pigs? Is there a farm?"

"No. Wild pigs. Sometimes they are around here."

"Wild pigs! You mean wild boar? Aren't they very fast and attack people?"

"That's right but you shouldn't run, okay? You should stand and shout at them while waving your arms."

With a quick glance into the forest to check there's nothing there, we both instinctively quicken our stride and...

"Race you up the hill!" Frank shouts, giving himself a head start.

Then for that brief, yet remarkable moment, the pain is gone and I am chasing Frank up the hill. Arms pumping, lungs burning, legs cycling!

Running is fantastic therapy! It helps us cope with our day-to-day stress with life, work, relationships, trauma and depression.

This is a true story. Frank Eppelman is one of my best friends and one of the nicest, kindest people you will ever meet. I have had the pleasure of working with him on various projects for over twelve years. Frank is the inventor of the Speed Court and the founder of Global Speed. His clients include many professional football and sports clubs around the world, including Bayern Munich, Real Madrid, RB Leipzig, Bayer Leverkusen Schalke, Adidas, and many more professional sports clubs, medical clinics and universities to boot.

Driving down from the forest, I said to Frank "This is one of those experiences you have to write down before you forget." So, I did.

There is another significant reason for telling this story. It was the last time I was able to run for more than twenty seconds. Soon after this run, I needed knee surgery again, just a few weeks later. My eighth.

I haven't been able to run since.

INTRODUCTION

The Story so far...

This is not an autobiography, so I will not be giving you a day-by-day account of what I have been doing for the last sixty-three years! What is relevant is that participating in sport and the injuries that I had as a youngster, created the passion that led me to setting up The Movement & Running School.

Mum got married at nineteen to my father, a Cypriot who she met at college. She had two kids by the time she was twenty-two and moved to Cyprus in 1957 from London. She couldn't speak the language, was not made welcome and we lived in a garage when I was born, until I was two years old.

She passed on her tenacity, appetite for hard work and her 'never give up attitude' onto her three sons.

We didn't have much as kids and football was our salvation. Like a lot of youngsters in the 60's with no television and no other distractions, we were outside every possible minute kicking a ball and if the ball deflated or broke, we replaced the inner tube with pieces of cloth and carried on playing. We played in the streets, off the walls, we played in the parks, we played in the house. We played until it was dark outside, and we couldn't see any more or until we were dragged inside by our mum.

My brother Chris, who is 3 years older than me, had joined the football academy of one of the top teams in Cyprus APOEL and was doing very well.

I joined the same football academy at twelve years old, after going through trials with loads of other kids. I wasn't very talented, but I made up for it with what I was good at. A lot of hard work, a lot of running and a determination to make it work. I turned up at all the training sessions whether I was injured or ill, whether I was playing or not.

My younger brother Andy was the talented footballer in the family. But he came close to not playing football at all. We used to take him with us to the local park where we played football for hours in the summer. The park was about a 20 minute walk, skip, run from our flat. He was two years old, and I was eight. We used to put him in the sand pit or at the side of the pitch and hand him some toy cars and only remember him on our way home - most of the time. Occasionally we would be half-way home, or about to cross a busy road and we would suddenly stop. "We forgot Andy!" and sprint back with our heart in our mouths until we found him.

I had recurring hamstring injuries on the right leg from the age of fifteen as well as a few other contact injuries and broken bones. It was a constant cycle of get injured, rest until the pain faded or you could tolerate it, get some 'friction' massage, start running up the stadium stairs, then join in with training. Get injured again and repeat the whole process. I broke my wrist at fifteen years old and they put it in plaster. I used to train with it during the week and cut the plaster off with some industrial shears at the weekend so I could play. Then duplicate the procedure the following week. I still struggle with my left wrist now!

I began to worry about movement, my movement, when I was seventeen. That is when I first injured my knee in a game.

The physio said it wasn't serious and we could help it along with a few injections that would stop the pain. Of course, I agreed. I had six weeks of training and playing with cortisone injections and then partly ruptured my ACL in an innocuous movement. They put my knee in plaster for six weeks.

Because I was determined to get back to playing football again, I trained relentlessly for six months. I made comeback after comeback, trying to play. Running in a straight line was okay, but as soon as I started twisting and turning, I was damaging muscles and ligaments further, until I eventually ruptured my ACL (Anterior Cruciate Ligament), PCL (Posterior Cruciate Ligament) and lateral knee ligaments.

I have had seven surgeries on the right knee and one on the left knee through compensating so much. After my third knee surgery at twenty-six, I was told by the consultant that I would need a knee replacement by the time I was forty. I still have my own knee, but only just! I didn't just accept the inevitable. I have been doing my own rehabilitation since my first surgery.

At nineteen, I came back to the UK. I didn't have enough money to go to university or polytechnic, frankly I didn't have the qualifications either. I was too busy playing football to study for my A-levels.

I applied for a few apprenticeships and eventually got a job as a 'Trainee Computer Operator' with a big manufacturing company in London. Computers were the up-and-coming technology in the late 70's. I worked hard at my day job over the next twenty years. Becoming a Computer Programmer, then Systems Analyst, then IT Manager. I moved into marketing with a British software company and started travelling across the world in the early 90's.

But I was determined if I couldn't play, I would coach. I began applying for football coaching courses at weekends, and then I enrolled on a part-time evening course, on 'fitness after injury' in London in 1980. The course was run every Monday evening from 6pm to 10pm and it was the spark that took me on a journey of coaching. I was twenty-two. In my spare time I trained to get fit, mainly running and strengthening my knee. I began to coach. I was always looking for more coaching courses. In those days, pre-internet, you had to call or write letters to national associations to get information or look up the local library's notice board to find anything interesting.

Coaching was a substitute to playing, but it was good substitute. It gave me a massive buzz to help other people return from injury or coach them and see it materialise in a game. I began coaching non-league football and run fitness classes in the evenings and at weekends, at schools, social clubs and youth clubs.

My Information Technology career went from strength to strength, and I became a senior executive with three different companies. I had the opportunity to travel the world and earn good money for my family.

But my passion was coaching and rehabilitation. I would spend up to twenty to thirty hours a week coaching part-time, evenings and weekends without payment. All the time working in a full-time job in IT.

The coaching was what I looked forward to. It gave me a purpose, a sense of satisfaction and fulfilment! I could not wait to come back from a trip and get straight into it. I would organise flights if I was travelling, so I would be at trainings sessions or games, even with jetlag.

I coached track athletes and footballers, but rehabilitation was what I was particularly fascinated with. Because of my injuries I wanted to find solutions. I could see certain athletes get recurring injuries just like I did. I knew the answer was not just rest, get some massage and try again. I could see that the advice given was inefficient and plain wrong, whether you were a fire fighter returning from injury, or a serious athlete, runner, or footballer.

I focused on movement. I observed how the athletes compensated when they walked and run. I would try to change their movement to see if that helped and made changes to their training. Mainly through trial and error and instinct.

I became passionate, make that fanatical, about movement. I read everything that I could get my hands on in libraries and bookshops. This was in the late 80's, before the internet, social media and websites. There was not a lot of information on coaching and rehabilitation around. I used to go into libraries and pick out anatomy and physiology books to try and find the link between what I was seeing in people's movement and the problems they had. I didn't make as much progress as I would have liked.

I had a strong belief in what I was coaching. I made a lot of mistakes, mainly on myself! But I discovered what worked and I was not afraid to change things if they didn't work. I began to get good results with individuals and amateur teams. I had a lot of success at developing running speed and helping people come back from injury. Through word-of-mouth recommendations, I began to work with various elite athletes and footballers. I would spend three to four evenings and weekends every week travelling to different places in London to coach.

I knew this is what I wanted to do. Coach full-time. But I also knew that I was a 'nobody' in sporting terms and no-one would give me a job in professional sport. I wrote to a lot of clubs offering my services as a speed coach to show what I could do. I did not get a single reply. I decided if I could not get a job in professional sport, I would create my own.

I started planning to set-up my own Speed & Rehabilitation Centre that would serve professional and amateur athletes of different sports, but I also wanted to help ordinary people who were not athletes. I thought I was a good coach. I was helping people get better and faster, so why not make a business out of my passion? Call it arrogance or confidence or both. I set up my first coaching company in 1994, working part-time in various locations initially.

When I mentioned my plans to some coaches and physiotherapists I was working with, I got a lot of cynicism; "You're crazy!" "It won't work." "Why would people come to a centre like that?"

It wasn't much better with family and friends; "You are going to give up your well-paid job to do what? Are you nuts?" My brother.

The exception was my wife, Thoulla. Her words were "If you are sure that is what you want to do, then do it."

Those who know me well know that, among my many annoying characteristics, I am also very obstinate. If you tell me I cannot do something, I will not give up until **I decide** I cannot do something.

In 1982 I went to see the film 'Gandhi' and I was inspired by his story and read everything I could about him.

One of his quotes made a big impression on me:

> *If I believe I cannot do something, it makes me incapable of doing it.*
> *But when I believe I can, then I acquire the ability to do it even if I*
> *did not have it in the beginning.* - Mahatma Gandhi

I copied the saying from one coaching notebook to another for years. When I set up the first Speed and Rehab Centre, I laminated the quote and stuck it up it on the wall by the superspeed treadmill. It is still above my desk. Nearly forty years after I first read it.

Still working full-time with a software company, I began to search for a suitable space. I signed a lease for what would be my own centre. It was in a cold, damp, and somewhat dark space, under the arches in Stamford Brook station in Chiswick, West London. The trains run above the centre and the whole place would shake and we had to raise our voices to be heard.

I remember taking Thoulla to see it when I signed the lease, I was so excited.

As we walked in, she said "What HAVE you done?"

But I could see beyond the mess and the cynicism, to what it could become. With a lot of sweat, not to mention blood and tears and most of our savings! I made the space work. For nearly a year I worked weekends and late into the night, painting damp walls, purchasing second-hand equipment, laying floors, stopping water leaks.

With no experience in taking my passion and making it into a business, I gave up my job as Vice President of Europe to coach full-time.

My first three customers were a Great Britain sprinter and two professional footballers. All three were injured.

Today as I write this, twenty-seven years after I began coaching profession-ally and as a business, we have coached over 60,000 people in our two London centers.

We see a huge variety of people and no two people are the same. We have grown mainly through recommendations. From six-year-old children with movement issues, to eighty-year-old hip replacements. Stroke survivors, people with neurological damage and brain injuries. Elite track and field ath-letes and professional athletes in football, rugby, tennis, basketball, handball, dance, ballet and other sports. Juniors, Seniors, Olympians, Gold Medalists, World Champions. Many extra-ordinary people who just want to move pain free after injury or just to be able to be the best they can be.

We have trained physical therapists and coaches in over forty Movement and Running School Clinics around the world and there are over one hun-dred certified Coaches, Therapists, Osteopaths, and Podiatrists practicing our Performance & Rehabilitation Methodology.

This book is about the method that we use to teach people how to run which, is only half of what we do. It has been hard for me to write, not because I had to decide what to put in it, but what to leave out. It has also been difficult because I am not a writer, I am a coach. I get motivated and enthusiastic when I am coaching, whether its running, speed or rehabilitation. That's what I like to do, and that's what you will find me doing every day, most days of the week, trying to give my best.

For me coaching means teaching, whether you are applying it to running, rehabilitation, a sports skill or performance. This philosophy is still at the heart of what we teach in our centres today.

There are five key values that I try to follow and teach. My kids get sick of hearing me repeat them!

- **Work hard at everything you do.** There is no substitute for hard work. It doesn't matter how talented you are, if you don't have the right work ethic you will not achieve your goals.

- **Don't give up.** Don't ever, ever, ever, give up. Get back up and start again.

- **Whatever happens don't feel sorry for yourself for long**. Don't believe that everyone is against you. Reset your thoughts and your values and go again.

- **Be humble.** Don't be arrogant. Do what you do for yourself, not for everyone else.

- **Be kind.** Help those who need help and don't expect anything in return.

This book is in two parts. The first is the philosophy behind how we change movement patterns and the importance of the brain and the nervous system in every movement we change.

The second part is the practical. The Running School Method. I explain step-by-step, how you can change your running technique. What exercises, drills and training programmes you can follow if you want to run better and faster. Let's go!

1

MOVE BETTER

We were designed to move!

Millions of years ago, as our human ancestors roamed the earth to forage, running became a way of life. We climbed mountains, jumped across streams and scrambled up ravines using our unique endurance capacity to chase prey into exhaustion. In this world, it was 'eat or be eaten.'

Mostly we walked. We were nomads on the move, never staying still for too long. Some think we even averaged 25km a day. For those of you who count your steps, that's about 40,000 steps a day, every day. Anthropologists and evolutionary biologists believe that the reason we have such a powerfully developed brain is because of movement. We learn about our environment and our world with every step we take.

Our brain is malleable through experience. It's important we keep using and challenging it. From the day we are born, our brain is informed, developed and enhanced through daily movement.

The evidence is abundantly clear that the more we move, the more our brain develops and changes. Continuous research in neuroplasticity, diseases, and general population health reveals that movement, exercise, and nutrition determine how we can live our lives better both physically and emotionally, but also how well we will age.

We are all wired differently. Our brain is not only shaped by our movement but our environment and our habits. Although we are all made of the same component parts, the wiring of our brain and our neuropathways is different in every single one of us.

The positive effects of regular movement and aerobic exercise on our cognitive and mental abilities have been tested thoroughly. Studies show that cognitive performance and long-term memory improve significantly with regular movement and aerobic exercise. That includes our focus and attention, the ability to solve problems, decision making, and learning new skills. Exercise has the exceptional capability to boost mental health but also to reduce cognitive deterioration in aging.

What is even more interesting is how the brain and the body can recover from years of being a couch potato as well as from illness. Positive results in physical, mental and cognitive performance, have been made in unfit individuals, who have taken up aerobic exercise. Big improvements were shown in less than eight weeks of beginning an exercise programme.

At our Speed & Rehabilitation Centre we work with many stroke survivors and people with neurological conditions or brain injuries. We are always fascinated and delighted to see how they develop and improve their functionality, their cognitive ability, and their quality of life as we help to retrain their movements through bespoke exercises. There is nothing more thrilling and life-affirming than witnessing their movement functionality improve, their cognitive abilities re-emerge, and their quality of life make giant leaps.

Many of us start panicking and begin hyperventilating at the words 'aerobic exercise.' We have visions of running for hours on end, or even worse, being forced to attend 'aerobic classes.'

The studies show that just 30 minutes of brisk walking per day is enough to improve your cognitive performance. If that isn't enough to get you off the couch, consider this:

In trials that have been replicated with thousands of people over the world, purposeful walking for thirty minutes every day can reduce your risk of some of the world's leading diseases, including:

- Dementia by 50%
- Alzheimer's by 60%
- Stroke by 60%
- And a whole range of cancers by 50%

If you think about your nutrition, eat healthily and add a couple of sessions of resistance and strength work every week, the benefits to longevity, both physical and cognitive, will be even greater.

"Walking is man's best medicine."

Hippocrates made that statement over 2600 years ago. This statement is more relevant today than it ever was in ancient Greece!

Hippocrates, known as the father of medicine, used to prescribe exercise and particularly walking, to all his patients. He based his medical practice on observations of the individual patient and the study of the human body.

He believed that all illnesses had a natural cause. At that time, most of the population believed that diseases were a punishment from the gods or caused by superstition. He recommended diet and physical exercise as remedies.

So why is this important to movement and running?

We are cross-lateral movers. When we move, we swing 'left-arm, right leg' and vice-versa. It's imprinted in us from the first few months in the womb, it's how we crawl as babies and how we walk as adults. Our brain fires up the nervous system, the nervous system fires up the muscles and the basis of human locomotion is triggered.

How we move as babies and children has a profound effect on how we move as adults. Our movement patterns are developed from when we are babies and change through our early years as we continue to grow, play, move and participate in sport.

We are unique movers in this world. We have three basic gaits;

- Crawling
- Walking
- Running

Crawling

Crawling is our first gait. With the shortest duration. Babies begin to lift their head from about one to three months old and experiment with rolling movements until about six or seven months when they begin to crawl. When we crawl, we move right knee and left hand and left knee and right hand to initiate the movement.

Not all babies develop at the same rate, so the timescales for crawling vary from baby to baby. But one thing is constant, we learn through repetition and error.

We stand up, fall down, reset, repeat the process, cry a bit and laugh a lot.

Then suddenly we take the first two staggering steps, fall down again and then repeat the whole process. Eventually, we manage to walk.

Walking

Walking is our principal and most extensively used gait. It is also our most functional movement, the one movement we do more than any other in day-to-day life.

Its benefits are plentiful and unending. But because of our habits and life-style, many of us don't realise we have actually forgotten how to walk efficiently!

"What do you mean many of us have forgotten how to walk? I know how to walk!" you might say.

Many of us, through habit, compensation or inactivity have developed an inefficient walking gait. Those of us who are living in big cities have changed our functional movement because of our modern lifestyle, our habits and our lack movement.

Running

Running is our survival gait. It is linked to our 'flight or fight' basic instinct. We used to run to catch food or run not to become food!

From ancient times, it used to be an indicator for bravery, achievement and stature in the community. Today it is still linked with a sense of achievement but more importantly, for many, it is great therapy and contributes to our survival in our stressful world.

24

What is the problem with modern movement?

Modern comforts are affecting our health. The use of cars, computers, video games, watching TV, excessive eating and drinking are all influencing our movement. When you also add a global pandemic and lockdown into the mix then the mental and physical health issues are multiplied exponentially.

The invention of the smart phone is probably the one piece of modern technology that has a long-term negative effect on movement. It is probably the best and worst invention of modern times. I talk about our dependence on our 'smart' phones in almost all the courses that we run on Movement Repatterning. I wrote a blog about the negative effects of the mobile phone on our movement patterns about ten years ago. I admit now that I was wrong. Unfortunately, it is a lot worse than I imagined.

One of the effects of our over reliance on technology is that we spend too much time sitting and not enough time moving. Most office workers sit down for between ten to twelve hours a day. First, we travel to work by train, by bus or car. Then a big part of the work is carried out sitting down, mostly staring at a computer screen. Then we travel back home by train, by bus or car again. If you look around you when you are on public transport you will see that, with very few exceptions, everyone is on their mobile phone.

As for relaxation, we sit down to engage with social media, watch television or play games almost always on our phone. For humans, home is no longer a sanctuary and respite from the daily battle for status because of social media. Kids are always in the battle for attention on social media.

We now have email and social media communication on our smart phones just in case we miss that vital life or death junk email. Someone trying to sell us something we don't need or a fascinating photograph posted on social media by someone we don't even know.

So even when we do walk, we have one or two hands occupied, sending text messages, reading emails, browsing or talking.

In many countries, the internet through broadband in the homes has been very accessible since the beginning of 2000. Smart phones have now been around for over twelve years and many people are lost if they do not have their phone in their hand. Unfortunately, a whole generation of young people are growing up dependent on and addicted to the internet. They are linked through their umbilical cord to their smart phone! It is now an attachment to their hand. Ok I am exaggerating a little, but you get the picture.

Walking is the most functional of all human movements and we are doing less and less of it.

We were born to move. We think better when we move, we learn better when we move, we feel better when we move, we get healthier when we MOVE!

What do we mean by better movement?

For centuries, the medical world was convinced that humans are born with a brain that did not change much during our lifetime. They believed that our movement patterns were fixed in a certain part of the motor cortex and could not be altered. Any damage to the brain either through impact or a neurological issue like a stroke, was irreversible.

Some brilliant medical experts and neuroscientists have since, unequivocally, proven that the brain is a dynamic structure that can change through stimulation and movement and reorganise itself to get better functionality.

Today this is known as 'neuroplasticity'. We all have unique movement patterns. Every individual moves differently. Our movement patterns have been shaped, molded, and perfected or 'imperfected' from the way we first begin to crawl, walk, run, and move every day. Our movement patterns are significantly affected by the number of hours we spend sitting down.

Yes, we all have the basic brain construction that allows us to do all the basic functions. The brain grows with learning, skills and movement. The more movement we undertake, the more wiring takes place and the more complex the brain becomes.

The more movement we participate in and the more learning we experience, whether it's playing a musical instrument, learning a new skill or language, exercising or participating in sport, the more the brain re-wires itself to record these experiences.

This means we all have unique movement patterns, shaped by our individual and daily movement. It's called our 'Functional Movement'. It shapes how we perform real-world tasks, using multi-joint, multi-planar movements.

The ease with which we achieve it is down to the 'Kinetic Chain' – how our connecting joints, bones and muscles work together to pull off such movements. The kinetic chain is what is impacted by habit and or injury.

Put all this together and it goes without saying that we all, therefore, have completely individual walking and running movements.

The human body is a truly incredible machine. To simply lift your foot takes countless neurons and chemical reactions in the blink of an eye, let alone when you want to propel your body forward into a run. But it's the order of events in the neuropathways that is vital - and it's in these most of the problems arise.

Let's look at the major contributors that define our movement in our lifetime:

Injury, Surgery or Illness

Anything that causes pain and disrupts our movement disrupts the kinetic chain of the body. This can also cause neural compensations which make us move differently and can put pressure on different parts of the body and its overall function.

This is pretty obvious when we are talking about a major disturbance to the way the body usually functions. An accident or a serious sporting injury, like a knee or ankle break, a sprain, or a neurological incident like a stroke, can cause a disruption to the way the brain accesses the motor map.

Habit or Inefficient Repetitive Movement

A disruption to our movement patterns could also be caused by an inefficient repetitive movement. For example, when we go for a run and we hold the phone or a bottle of water in our left hand, it leads to not moving that arm as much and influences the stride length on the opposite leg. This means we have one stride longer than the other, putting more body weight through one side over the other, subsequently increasing the stress on one side, you guessed it, over the other!

When we run the brain continuously makes adjustments to our running to account for this, it then becomes a habit and the movement map changes. The brain can cope with this if it is not overstressing the kinetic chain. You may get a bit of muscle tightness or pain, but it goes away when you rest. However, if you increase the frequency, volume or intensity of your running you may begin to get repetitive movement pain. Then the brain will start to make adjustments to reduce the load.

A similar disruption can occur in walking. If you carry a heavy bag on one side all the time or you are constantly on your phone looking down when you are walking, this becomes a habit and if repeated enough times, your new movement pattern.

Our ability to move, walk, run, jump, reach out, bend down, twist, spin and any other movement you can imagine doing, is driven from the most complex and intricate maps located in our brain!

These series of movement maps are managed by the brain within our primary motor cortex - the region that controls all voluntary movement. The sensory receptors in our body are also linked to each other via 'body maps' – the foot map is linked to the shin map, which is linked to the knee map, which is linked to the hip map, etc. All the way to the top of the body.

All left side movements are initiated from the right side of the brain and all right sided movements are initiated from the left side of the brain.

When we move, this interconnected series of sensory relationships is controlled automatically based on information the brain receives from the ground up, from our proprioceptive sensors at the bottom of the feet and from our peri-personal space. We have tens of thousands of sensors in the sole of each foot. When we stand or move this is the only part of our body that interacts with the ground.

Peri-personal space is the space around our body from the top of our head to the end of our fingertips and toes and within reach of our limbs.

As we move, our proprioceptive system, which gives feedback to the brain about our body position in space and in motion, takes information from our interaction with the ground and our relationship with gravity.

It sends messages through the nervous system to the brain and the brain responds by making changes. For example, if we step on a stone and lose our balance it directs a correction to shift our balance to the opposite side to regain our footing.

It is so seamless, we don't even realise that it is going on. The corrections and adjustments are being made automatically to protect us from getting injured - until something happens, and we experience pain.

There are two main types of proprioceptive cells when it comes to movement. The first is entrenched into our muscles and tendons, and our brain uses the information to deduce the location of the limbs. The other kind is embedded in our joints and cartilage and sends information to the brain on the load that goes through the limbs, the mobility and position of our joints. We will talk about the importance of proprioception and the affect it has on our body, later in this book.

When we move the brain takes in information visually, auditorily and kinesthetically. It analyses the information to make any adjustments or reactive actions.

The job of the brain is to keep us safe and to keep us moving to achieve an objective!

The Pathway of a Movement

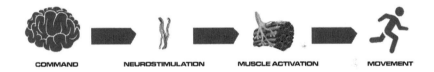

When we initiate a movement the brain will send a signal to the nervous system to begin the activation process. The nervous system will access the body maps, 'fire' the correct neuropathways and identify which muscles groups are needed to make the movement. The motor neurons will, in turn, activate the muscles and the movement ensues.

This of course, happens in a lot less time than it takes to explain the process!

So, if you imagine for a moment that you are a microscopic brain cell inside the command centre of the brain, the motor cortex, you will witness a scene that goes something like this:

Brain – "Okay team, we need to pick that toy up from the floor, access the movement map that has all the command links. Visual system engaged; Vestibular system ready!"

Nervous System – "Neurons get ready to assume firing positions; muscles get ready to move."

Motor Neurons – "OKAY muscles, YOU, YOU and YOU are going to carry out the movement with us - lets GO, GO, GO!"

And the individual steps forward, picks up the toy from the floor and places it in the box.

MOTOR NEURON

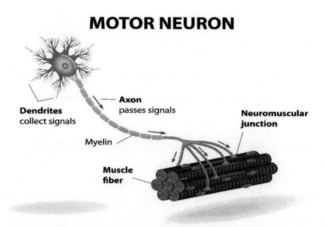

The nervous system travels via the spinal cord selecting the groups of muscles that will be needed for the movement. The neurons will attach themselves to the muscles and begin firing, causing the muscle to activate.

Your spinal cord is the central pillar of your nervous system, connecting your brain to the rest of the body via hundreds of thousands of nerves that spill out from it. At the other end of many of those nerves are your muscles.

The movement, if everything is working okay, is fluid, quick and precise. But if there are interruptions, for example due to pain or muscles not firing in the correct sequence, then the proprioceptive system will give feedback to the brain to make the necessary adjustments.

The motor neurons are amazing microscopic cells. They consist of a nucleus which is surrounded by the cell body. They have tentacles that send electrical signals to stimulate the muscles to wake them up and get them to activate.

Motor neurons are very sociable cells, they like to work in groups and are constantly linking up to make the activations faster. This linking up connection is called a synapse.

They're not just sociable they're incredibly clever too. They continuously monitor your movement and bring in more friends to their neighbourhood when a muscular pattern is repeated enough. They will even insulate their cabling (the axon) to make sure the electrical signals are at peak performance.

When everything is working smoothly the different movement maps in the brain get updated regularly. This movement map is called a 'motor engram', which is the way the brain 'memorises' regular movement patterns used to perform a movement or skill.

The neurons are doing their job and the muscles are firing in sequence and getting more efficient, faster and stronger. Our walking is efficient, our running movement is fluent, we can exercise at will and participate in fitness and in sports.

Our movement maps get created through repeated stimulus. So how we walk, how we run and how we repeat every-day tasks like walking, reaching, bending, squatting and sitting all contribute to the brain creating the motor engram.

It is important to remember that when an engram is formed, the next time it is required, the brain will fire the same neuropathways and our body will be able to perform that specific activity unconsciously. All this is scientific proof that moving matters, that injury recodes the body, that the movements you make in childhood have lasting effect, but that the body can be taught new tricks.

We will discuss running movement patterns in more detail later on in the book, including how our distinct walking and running patterns are associated with specific inefficiencies but also specific injury locations. Again, this is because our running patterns have been created into a specific movement map which is unique to each of us.

Myelin

There are very few things that will make a neuroscientist go weak at the knees. Myelin is one of them!

The brain consists of grey matter and white matter – a big gooey lump of nerve cells. Their behaviour up here results in everything that makes us human. In general, white matter consists of the nerve cells with insulated electrical cabling running down the length of their axons. This incredible biological material is called myelin, a chemical choreography of proteins and fat cells that are whitish in colour. Grey matter is grey because it lacks the wondrous myelin.

Neurons perform poorly without the myelin and that can have a profound effect on your movement. Myelin doesn't just speed up the signal, it improves the signals. Scientists have even discovered that myelin is vital even when you're still in the womb. It increases as we learn to crawl, walk and even talk. It's fundamental to our cognition, learning and behaviour throughout life.

So, when something changes in your myelin, you know about it…

But what happens when something goes wrong?

When we move there is a continuous feedback and feed-forward process going on between the brain, the nervous system, the proprioceptive system and the muscles and joints.

Was the movement efficient? Was it successful? Did it need correcting? Was the objective achieved? Was there pain? The nervous system takes all this information and reports back to the brain, where the motor engrams are activated, re-organised or changed according to the feedback data it receives.

When pain is present, the signals from the brain to the nervous system begin to change and the brain must make decisions to protect us from further damage and to help with recovery.

Compensation

If, when you bend down to pick up the toy, you have back pain, the brain sends the signal to the nervous system to adjust the movement. The nervous system begins to switch off certain neuropathways which are associated with the movement and the pain. We then change the way we bend down to pick up the toy.

The same applies if you are running and you are feeling calf or Achilles' tightness or pain on your right leg but, you keep running. Your brain will start to change your movement to reduce the load that is put through the right side. It will shift the weight onto the opposite side to off-load the stress to reduce the pain and you start to limp. The changes it makes to compensate are not just to the lower body but also to the upper body.

One of the major roles of the brain is to protect us from catastrophic injury. If pain is present, it will make changes to avoid the pain by slowing down the movement, shifting the weight onto the other limb or bending or reaching in a different way.

If the pain persists for a period of time, the neurons begin to uncouple from the muscle fibre and the synapses begin to weaken and then drift apart.

The brain then adjusts the movement map to fire the 'adjusted' neuropathways and carry out a different movement, activating different neuropathways.

This, in turn, causes a disruption to the firing sequence of the muscles and we get imbalances, poor coordination, and continuous compensation and in the case of injury or surgery, the muscles begin to atrophy.

This is why, when you return from a strain or other injury, which has kept you from running for some time, your movement can be slow, and compensatory. You feel as if you have forgotten how to run. Which is not far from what is actually happening! We regularly see runners who come to see us after injury, who are limping but have no pain. In most cases they are also landing differently on one foot compared to the other.

What happens if there is inactivity?

It's not just pain that causes over-compensation. Inactivity, poor habitual posture and inefficient movement over a period of time will also change the signals and adjust the neural map.

Sitting down 10-12 hours per day or using the same muscle groups repeatedly in a certain way, like in shuffle running and walking without using the arms, will cause the brain to change the movement map and this in turn leads to sensory motor amnesia.

This is where the brain and the nervous system are slow in activating certain muscle groups because of habit, or pain. The firing sequence of certain muscle groups is disrupted, and they are not firing correctly.

It's as if the brain is saying: "Okay John (not his real name) if this is the way we want to walk or run, I will adjust the way everything works and update the Movement Map."

Our brain is steered, affected and influenced by several things during our lifetime but there are certain behaviours which can affect our movement maps:

- Our daily movement patterns
- Inactivity
- The training we do for fitness or sport
- The environment in which we live and work
- How the nervous system fires and recruits, muscles, and organs
- What we eat and drink

When movement combinations occur - that is where groups of muscles contract together - the motor map in the brain, which represents the movements, expands. This indicates the correlation of movements and muscles can be stimulated, recruited, re-organised and the motor system changed.

Neuroscience research has made astonishing strides to uncover how we can change both the damaged brain, but also how we can change our habits and activities and influence a change in the intact brain.

So why is this important for running?

Neuroscientists believe that neuroplasticity is not only the basis of how we learn new skills and enhance existing ones but is also vital in the rehabilitation of the muscles and bones, the damaged brain and the nervous system.

So, neuroplasticity is especially important after injury to reduce compensations which will decrease chances of re-injury. When we rehabilitate it's not just a matter of working on the injured body part. We need to rehabilitate or correct the whole body and its movement patterns throughout the kinetic chain.

This is also the basis for re-education of movement and improving our walking and running technique.

The studies prove unquestionably that the brain and the nervous system are able to adapt and regenerate. That motor neurons and other brain cells have the incredible ability to change their structure in response to our behaviour, movement and external influence.

We call this process of re-educating the movement maps 'Movement Re-patterning.' This is the methodology we use at The Running School for our rehabilitation after injury or surgery, and to re-educate walking and running movement.

SUSANNAH'S STORY

Susannah Gill
World Marathon Challenge – Record Holder

"Let Mike change your life."

I can split my time on earth into two parts – BM and AM. That is to say, 'Before Mike' and 'After Mike', such is the profound effect he has had on my life.

Before I met Mike, I was a dedicated runner, but also a broken runner. I had completed about two dozen marathons and a handful of ultras, even going under three hours for the London Marathon in 2015, but my word it hurt!

I loved running as much as I do now, but I had got used to spending a lot of time feeling pretty sore. The lovely long runs at weekends would give way to aching hips, creaking knees and cramping feet. I thought all of this was simply what you had to go through to run marathons. I thought it was part of being a runner.

To my surprise, but absolutely inevitably, I eventually injured myself to the point where I could not run. My left knee had sharp shooting pains that I simply could not run through. This was caused by damaged cartilage which was floating around my knee like pieces of eggshell. This is a fairly common running injury, primarily caused by letting my feet run 'on one track' so my knees were constantly having to work at an angle which hinge joints do not like doing.

Doctors can work wonders and I had the cartilage removed and was off running again but it did not feel good. I would trip over far too often and the aches and pains were just as bad as before.

I knew something was wrong, but I did not know what and, crucially, I did not know how to fix it. I saw a reference for The Running School and thought I might as well give it go.

And so my life – and running – moved from the BM phase and into the AM phase. In doing so I want to make clear I am not special, and I have not learnt anything more than thousands of fellow Running School students have over the years but – wow – it has changed my life!

From my first session I learnt about the heel cycle being key to engaging glutes and hamstrings. I learnt to run with my feet on two clear tracks to stop tripping myself up and upsetting my knees. I stopped rolling my shoulders and started using my arms to set the rhythm for my legs. I ran taller and more comfortably.

Alongside this I learnt about the importance of strength work and completed mobility exercises I still do on a weekly basis.

All of this does not stop aching muscles after a long run, but I ache in all the right places. Rather than my hips and knees being sore and my feet cramping, my hamstrings and glutes do the heavy lifting and have grown bigger, making me stronger and more stable.

I am still a dedicated runner, but I am also a happier runner. I have also become braver which was the catalyst for my greatest adventure, running World Marathon Challenge - 7 marathons in 7 days on 7 continents - and setting the world record for the feat in 2019 with an average marathon time of 3 hours 28 minutes,

Without Mike I would never have dared take on this challenge, let alone known how to get myself ready for the most unique 168 hours of my life. Throughout this challenge Mike was my coach, mentor, agony aunt and friend. He looked after me mentally and physically. He helped me get more out of myself than I ever knew was possible. He gave me a story to tell in a book, and simply put, I would not be the person I am today without having met Mike.

The real magic of this story is that there is no magic in it at all. The secret is there is no secret.

Mike can apply his immense expertise and unique skills to any of us. From marathon runners to stroke recoverees, from five-year-olds to eighty-five-year-olds, Mike is the person you need to know if you want to move better.

Mike: We occasionally read in the media, about recreational runners, who have a fulltime job, who train on their own, who love running for the thrill of it. Who enter races to challenge themselves and because it is more interesting than running on your own. Then they get injured and are broken. That is when they realise how much running means to them.

In the movie script version of the story, the recreational runner is so determined to get back to running that they dedicate every spare minute to getting back to fitness. They sign up to race after race to make up for lost running time. Then in a time of unwavering excitement, decide to sign up to one of the worlds hardest running challenges. Our runner, both scared and excited by the challenge, is driven to train like an Olympic athlete. Training seven days a week as if their life depended on it, just to be able to survive the race. At the finale of the movie, against all the odds, the runner wins the race and breaks the world record at the same time. A classic inspiring Hollywood movie!

It hasn't been made into a movie yet!

But in 2019, Susannah Gill, achieved something similar. She competed and won the World Marathon Challenge and broke the world record for running 7 Marathons in 7 Days on 7 continents. If you want to be inspired, you can read the story, in her own words in her book; 'Running Around the World, How I Ran, 7 Marathons, in 7 days on 7 Continents'.

The mental strength, grit, determination, and a stubbornness that never allowed herself to miss a day's training during her preparation, are only part of the story. Anyone interested in running at any level, should read the book. They will want to put their trainers on and go out for a run after reading her running story.

I first met Susannah in 2017. A dedicated recreational runner, who had run different distances including a few marathons. She came to see us, because she couldn't get back to her running 'groove' following knee surgery. She loved running, but never followed any structured training programme. Like a lot of runners with a full-time job she would do a few short runs during the week and a longer run on the weekend. But she was an enthusiastic runner and very determined to improve herself and went from running 3:46 in her first marathon to 2:58, 7 years later. But with quite few injuries along the way. Before she came to see us, she had inexplicably tripped over a few times when running and had hurt her knees, hands and face, but more importantly, it had affected her confidence.

When we analysed Susannah's running biomechanics, we found that she had compensated so much, before and after her surgery that she was crossing over. Instead of running on two separate 'tracks' she was crossing over the midline of the body with her right leg. During contact time with the ground, this puts the full weight of the body through the joints that are not in alignment, putting stress on the foot, ankle, knee, hip and back. She wasn't using her arms correctly, rotating too far across her axis and leaning too far forward when running. If that wasn't enough, her left leg would internally rotate when she got tired and kick her right leg. That was the main reason she was stumbling. She was in pain after every longish training run and very stiff in the hips, quads and upper thoracic after every race struggling to get up and down stairs.

I have worked with many elite athletes over the past 30 years including Olympic gold medallists and world champions in different sports. Susannah is up there with the best of them!

2

MOVEMENT RE-PATTERNING

How does it work?

'Movement Re-patterning' is based on neuroplasticity. We know from years of medical evidence that the human brain is very plastic, that means it can change and regenerate, as long as there is breath and movement left in the body.

Neuroplasticity is the ability of the brain and the nervous system to rewire its connections and change the movement maps in the brain. The brain and the nervous system are designed to link together to control the internal workings of the body but also how we move and interact with the world.

We use it when teaching people how to run better and run faster, but we also use it extensively for rehabilitation after injury or surgery and with stroke patients and those with neurological issues.

To do this we have to re-educate our movement patterns. This is done by correcting the movement asymmetries and cross lateral movement patterns. Stimulating the proprioceptive system and the nervous system to activate the correct muscle groups and to fire in the correct sequence. This will enhance an individual's functional movement.

Once we have achieved that, then we stimulate the nervous system to increase the recruitment speed of the motor unit.

One of the questions I get asked frequently; "Is it possible to teach someone a new running technique when they have been running in a certain way for years?"

If we can teach a stroke patient to walk again, years after the stroke, then teaching someone to run more efficiently is simple.

It is simple, but it is not easy.

It is not enough to try the process once and then think that the new movement will be rewired in the brain. It simply does not work that way.

The brain and the nervous system can change in response to behaviour, practice, and experience. The same process applies to running technique, as it does for rehabilitation after injury or surgery however, it just takes a little longer with rehabilitation.

When it comes to movement re-patterning and re-educating running technique, we know that it takes approximately six to eight weeks to change someone's running technique to make it an 'unconscious movement map'. It does not change by just thinking about it. It also doesn't work, if you watch a couple of videos before your next run and try to implement what you think you understood.

There are a few individual necessities:

1. You need to have a desire to change
2. You need to have the motivation to make changes
3. You need to undertake Concentrated Practice – Focusing on the technique of the movement
4. You need to practice, practice and practice
5. You need to eat, recover, and sleep well

The first questions we ask when runners and patients come to see us are: "What are your objectives? What do you want to achieve and what is your motivation?" The answers range from:

- I want to stop getting injuries
- I want to run more efficiently

41

- I want to run faster
- I want to be able to eat more chocolate
- I hate running and I find it painful

Having the motivation to change is critical to effectively changing the brain map and the nervous system. You must want to change your behaviour or your movement. Anyone who is not motivated will not focus for long periods of time and change does not take place.

Focus and practice go together. The brain learns quicker when we focus on one task and concentrate on the practice. The brain builds movement maps and skill maps. It tries to pass motor tasks to the reflexive part of the brain to conserve energy.

These are the motor tasks that do not require concentration, because we have done them thousands of times before. Tasks like picking up a glass, walking, turning to reach for something, bending down to pick something up. Because the motor map is so engrained through practice, we use reflexive behaviour and movements.

The early stages of learning a new skill are more stressful and more tiring. This is because the brain must deal with a new skill and at the same time keep the rest of our functions in operation. The brain must figure out, how long the skill is going to take, process the new instructions, and then cope with the fatigue that comes with practicing a new skill.

This is what we call 'conscious incompetence'. When learning a new running technique, the brain must cope with controlling the heart, the lungs, the muscles, the way the arms move, the way the legs move and make changes to the movement map. It begins to secrete different chemicals that cause stress as well as excitement in the process of learning something new. So, in the beginning it is more tiring for the individual, physically and mentally.

Repetition matters. The more we perform a concentrated practice and repeat the process, the quicker the brain creates the map. If our athlete is also unfit, then the priority of the brain will be to keep the heart and the lungs working, so a lot of energy is taken up with basic protection and our runner tires quickly.

We advise athletes to practice the new skill in small chunks, but runners are keen to advance too quickly and don't always listen to advice.

We coached an elite female triathlete, following a referral from her physio-therapist. She was accompanied by her husband, also a triathlete. We performed a biomechanical analysis and I described what I could see as part of the problem and explained the process of re-educating her running technique and what she had to do. She turned to her husband and said, "You should do this as well, you have more issues than I have!". He declined saying "I'm okay, I don't need to change my form; it works for me."

A few weeks later and making good progress with her running she said smiling, "Oh my husband is going to book in to see you, he injured his hamstring. He was trying to change his technique on his own, during a 10K run and thoroughly confused himself!" The triathlete only focused on changing one side of his leg cycle, the left side he thought was the weaker of the two.

We helped the triathlete rehab his hamstring strain and then we re-educated his running technique.

The process of making a change is important, and the process works better if we don't cut corners.

Neuroplasticity is triggered with focus and deliberate practice and completed during rest and recovery, particularly when we sleep. The brain uses more energy when we sleep, because it is rewiring and figuring out what goes where. Which is why it is important to plan our training and recovery.

We work with a lot of different people at our centres, from athletes with minor injuries like strains, to very serious musculoskeletal injuries following surgery and also those who have suffered strokes, brain damage or cancer.

I am continuously amazed by how the brain re-organises and re-generates its lost function to get the body moving again after major injury. I am full of admiration and humbled by the inner strength of people, of all age groups, who never give up, those who put in endless hours of rehabilitation to get moving, to get walking again, or back to running.

You may ask, what is the relevance of movement rehabilitation after a stroke and teaching runners how to run better and run faster. It is extremely relevant. Both physically and psychologically.

Non-athletes who experience dysfunction and pain, and athletes who get injured frequently experience motor losses. Not as serious as with a stroke patient, but enough to interrupt the movement patterns and get the athlete to compensate. The brain will always try to get the body moving and if there is pain, it will look for the path of least resistance to avoid the pain, which consequently leads to inefficient movement.

What happens after injury? How does the brain and the nervous system change to adapt to pain?

In a running or sporting context, there are three conditions which affect movement patterns:

1. Pain associated with sporting injuries like torn or strained muscles, or a musculoskeletal injury through impact or after surgery
2. Overuse or repetitive inefficient movements like running with a shuffle, twisting, or overstriding
3. When there is pain present due to stiffness or lack of mobility, for example in the neck or tight shoulders, hips, or lower back

The brain knows that to survive, it must keep us moving and so it tries to compensate to avoid pain. It changes the way it sends a message to the injured limp by changing the way the neuropathways recruit the different muscles tendons and how the joints move.

Here is what may happen, for example, with a runner who has a calf strain: on walking they will take shorter steps to avoid putting too much weight through the injured limb. When running they will consciously try to land flat footed or on the ball of the foot and then shift the weight onto the non-injured side. This will cause a change in how the body coordinates movement and changes the balance, with the opposite limb taking more strain.

During running movement, the motor system is sending signals to the brain via the nervous system and continuously assessing if it can move forward or not. If there is too much pain, then the brain will send the signal to stop or change the speed of the movement or landing impact to alleviate the pain.

So, if you are a runner should you perhaps be taking an extensive course in anatomy and physiology and learn how the nervous system works to run better or faster?

No! Do not panic!

However, there is a need to know if your movement is efficient or not, based on what your objective is and what you are trying to achieve. Most runners have not been taught how to run; they pick things up from other runners or through reading, or simply how they feel when they run. It is hard to coach yourself and be objective and change the movement patterns even if you do know what to change.

One of the amazing things about humans is that every move we make in every second of every minute, every day of every week, every month in every year, is a UNIQUE MOVEMENT.

That is one of the reasons why running technique is unique to every individual.

We have three sets of 'drivers':

- The arms and hands
- The legs and feet
- The head and the eyes

Depending on which driver we lead with, the brain and the central nervous system recruit different neural maps. These neural maps are influenced by several different factors:

- How fast we carry out the movement
- The direction we are travelling: forwards, backwards, sideways, up-wards, or downwards
- Whether we are moving in free motion – or holding or carrying an object
- Whether we are running, kicking, pushing, jumping, pulling, or thrusting

If you run and don't use your arms very much, then the brain recruits different neuropathways to what it would if you used your arms correctly.

During running, our motor system collects and processes information about the environment, the surface, and the internal movement patterns both mechanical and neural. This is our friend 'proprioception' again; the body's ability to perceive its location in space.

The proprioceptive system gives us feedback through sense and our eyes to make changes to the limbs to keep us upright, balanced and moving towards our goal. Most of the information is processed unconsciously and the brain takes all this information and decides how far, how long or how fast it can run. Feedback is continuous and it is essential to the refinement of movement patterns and re-education.

However, excessive movements when running, due to inefficiency, muscle imbalances or incorrect muscle activation can lead to overuse injury and inefficient running economy.

Runners have a deeply passionate, intense connection to their running movement as they have spent years creating it! This can often be the problem!

Any inefficiency will cause compensation and the brain will find a way to keep moving forward, so it will start to use different muscle groups to take the load if one muscle is tight or not activating correctly.

Elite and professional athletes, who perform at high intensity and high speeds, compensate as well. But because they have a lot of experience and can adjust their movement and are strong and incredibly determined, it is more difficult to identify and correct – until they get injured!

Why is there an issue with compensation if the athlete continues to train and compete when injured?

Through compensation, the kinetic chain begins to change, it begins to overload certain muscle groups and joints and eventually it leads to a plateau of performance and or injury.

When we analyse running injuries, we find that it is not that one simple issue that causes the problem. Just like it is never one simple change that will correct the problem. Re-educating movement patterns and correcting left to right asymmetries are key to fixing these problems.

Movement Re-Patterning - The process

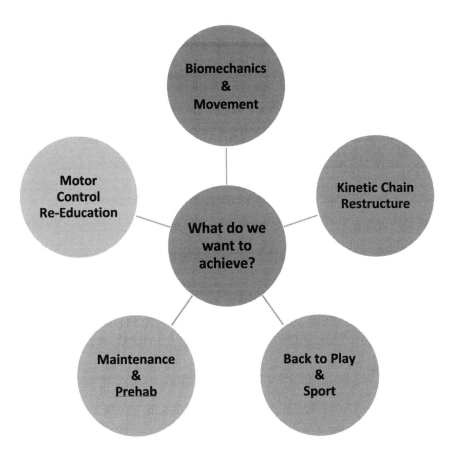

We apply the movement re-patterning methodology to rehabilitation, walking, running and speed. It is about re-educating the motor control - the control of movement through sensory information. We always look at an individual's functional movement *and* their walking *and* running biomechanics during the analysis, using our methodology.

The movement re-patterning methodology is based on what I call, five phases of neuromuscular re-education.

Phase One – Analysing Biomechanics and Movement

We analyse the individual with a series of functional movements to see how they move day-to-day. We begin to identify their compensations, if they have any, and if they feel pain when they move. We video the whole process and then sit down to study their movement and look at the movement patterns together. This includes their walking biomechanics and their functional movement. The functional movement analysis looks at how they bend or reach to pick something up, how they step forward and backward and how they rotate their body.

For runners, we analyse: their running technique, how they respond when they are tired and how they perform single leg movements. When we work with athletes - professional, recreational, young or master's level - we always try and replicate the game or race pace.

One of the key elements of the biomechanical analysis that we test during this process, is how the proprioceptive system responds to our interaction with the ground. This will be explained later in this chapter.

Along with the history of illness or injury and their current training regime, this helps us to 'draw the picture' of how the body and the neuromuscular system responds during movement.

Not all the analysis may be possible or necessary, particularly if we have someone who has a neurological issue or has pain. We would go straight to Phase 2 to begin the motor control re-education. You must remember that everyone is different and wired differently.

I was recently speaking with Adrian Chiles - journalist, television and radio presenter - during his show on BBC Radio 5 Live. It was a piece about running and injuries. I had worked with Adrian about six years ago when he came to me to improve his running overall and I started by analysing his movement.

Adrian still remembers the Biomechanical Analysis.

He wrote an article about it in the Guardian and spoke about it on the radio. In his words: "The most bizarre thing was my arms. The left one pumped backwards and forwards, while the right arm pumped to and from across my body. I could not believe that I moved like that. When I walked, only the left arm moved."

"Do you carry a shoulder bag much?" I asked.

"Yes." He said.

"On the right side?"

"Yes!"

"That may be the issue. It's a habitual movement."

This is something many of us do on a regular basis.

In his walking movement he was not moving the right arm. In his running, his right arm was going across the body, rather than backwards. The first thing we did with Adrian was correct his walking movement to get the functionality back on the right shoulder and correct his asymmetrical stride length. Only then did we begin to change the running technique.

Phase Two - Kinetic Chain Re-education

Our body functions like a chain. This chain is an integrated unit which consists of the various joints and segments of the lower body and upper body, the muscles that support the joints and the central nervous system. The kinetic chain drives everything in a fluid, unconscious motion. But only when everything is working okay.

The brain controls all movements, based on information that it receives from visual, kinesthetic and proprioceptive feedback.

I described earlier that, as humans, when we move, we move contralaterally. We move left arm and right leg simultaneously and right arm and left leg simultaneously. This contralateral movement is important to understand for several reasons, but the critical ones are as follows:

- The brain initiates all right sided movements from the left side of the brain and vice versa.
- The brain constantly monitors the position and movement of the body.
- Movements from one part of the kinetic chain influence other parts of the kinetic chain.
- The contralateral movements influence our daily movement patterns, mobility, stability and balance.

Each of our joints has a primary and secondary role to play in how the kinetic chain functions:

Foot — Stability

Ankle — Mobility

Knee — Stability

Hip — Mobility

Lumbar Spine — Stability

Thoracic Spine — Mobility

Scapula — Stability

Gleno-Humeral Joint — Mobility

Elbow — Stability

So, if we are looking at someone who has pain and not moving correctly, the cause of the problem is rarely where the pain manifests itself!

If a runner comes to see us with knee pain, we don't just treat the knee. We also assess the instability and mobility of the ankle and the hip joints and test the effect these have on balance and muscle activation. When I run rehabilitation courses for medical practitioners, I always say "You can treat where the patient is feeling the pain, but you will rarely fix the problem if you don't look at the whole kinetic chain."

I was recently analysing a professional footballer who was getting repeated hamstring injuries on his right side for twelve months. His physiotherapist described the history of leg and foot injuries over the previous two years and the rehabilitation that they had completed.

We carried out all the functional movement and speed tests and when we analysed the video clips I went through with the player and the physiotherapist what I observed, "The right leg is hitting the ground at a greater force than the left and is making a chopping motion during deceleration. The reason for this is because his left shoulder is over-rotating, because he is not using his left arm efficiently and, therefore, he is compensating with his opposite side."

They both looked at each other. The footballer had injured his left shoulder during a game fourteen months previously, before he started to get repetitive hamstring injuries on the right leg. The kinetic chain was interrupted.

Phase Three - Motor Control Re-education

To make effective corrective changes, we utilise the plasticity of the nervous system and, particularly, the proprioceptive system to change the neural map in the brain. This will give us better movement efficiency.

The proprioceptive system is critical to how we can change the motor programme. Sensory information, both external and internal, are stimulated by sensory triggers in both feedback and feedforward situations.

When we move, the body has two feedback systems:

- The proprioceptors located in the muscles, tendons, and skin provide information about internal mechanical events; and
- The exteroceptors are stimulated through vision and hearing which provide information about the environment

When we move, the two feedback systems work together. The brain combines all the internal and external data and determines force of muscular contraction, direction, and the speed you will move with.

But here's the interesting part. The processing of all that sensory information is happening both consciously and subconsciously. Most of this information is processed at the innate reflex level that you don't even notice – that is, a response learned through habit.

And habit leads to inefficient patterns many of us have.

The first three phases of correcting biomechanics, motor control re-education and kinetic chain restructuring can all be trained together. We do not need to separate them into different processes.

- We train the movements not the muscles. To do this, we re-educate our runners with total body movements
- Ensure that the posterior and anterior kinetic chains are functioning together
- Ensure that our activation exercises are working in groups

- Mobility is an especially important part in changing the movement patterns
- Repetition is key

We can retrain the movements, ensure the kinetic chain is operating with the least amount of stress and change the neural map for better motor control - all by implementing specific exercises, drills and technique changes.

Phase Four - Return to play or return to sport

Returning to play or sport is where we train functional movement, individual strength, endurance, speed, acceleration, and deceleration. Depending on what we are trying to achieve, the sport of the individual, and the level of the athlete, specific adaptations and demands are required. Efficient biomechanics and re-education of the motor system are crucial to enhancing and changing movement maps.

However, there are other important factors which need to be taken into consideration such as: i) Muscle strength and the interaction with the ground during dynamic movements. This is important for preventing injury to the same limb, but also a reduction in the likelihood of a compensation injury; ii) Good joint mobility also allows for better efficiency of the muscles and together they ensure we move better. When a joint is stiff, it restricts the ability of the muscles to move through their normal range of movement; iii) Speed, both straight line and multi-directional, can only be improved and enhanced by working fast and stimulating the nervous system. How the athlete adapts to the interaction and forces with the ground, when running, turning, jumping and decelerating.

Phase Five - Maintenance

When we have corrected the movement patterns and the individual is back to functional movement and running, it does not mean they are now injury-proof. Once the pain is gone, humans have a tendency to forget what processes, tools and exercises we used to get us pain free and back to sport or function.

Once you have fixed the problem, you need to re-check, at regular intervals, that the patterns have not changed again. You need to keep working and tweaking the movements.

RACHEL'S STORY

Rachel Hunt
Serious Amateur Runner

I started running approximately fifteen years ago at about the age of thirty. Prior to running my main sports were football and squash but after a frustrating series of groin injuries, I took up running as anything in a straight line didn't seem to cause me any issues. It didn't take long before I was hooked on running and ventured into the world of racing and that's where my running injuries began.

When I look back over the years, there's not many running injuries that I haven't had. I've experienced ITB issues, high hamstring tendinopathy, lots of calf and Achilles issues, groin pain, quad and hamstring strains, right hip pain, constant lower back pain, foot issues and most of all persistent knee pain, you'd think I'd have given up!

With so many issues, I switched over from running to triathlon thinking that less running and less impact might help and to some degree it did, but I also started to pick up other niggles. I was extremely frustrated as I'd train hard for an event then get injured or have to put up with knee pain that would get worse as the mileage increased. I remember it being normal to hobble sideways down the stairs after a long run!

My turning point was following Bolton Ironman in 2012. It wasn't actually an injury that prompted my desire to seek help. I trained really hard for this event and although I completed it injury free and in a time I was really pleased with, I felt physically broken at the end. I needed to understand how I could become stronger and more efficient so that I could race these distances and finish in better condition.

I read books on run technique and strength training and did a few courses which helped but left me with more questions than answers and I still wasn't running injury free. I began to question whether running was right for me.

Roll on to approximately five years ago when I was scrolling through the internet on my continued search for help. I came across the Running School and their '2-day Functional Biomechanics of Running' course and

I signed up immediately. This was the best thing I have ever done! It was EXACTLY what I needed!

I remember having my initial video analysis and I was hoping that my run technique wouldn't be too bad as I had been working on reducing my overstride. Boy was I in for a shock! I didn't think I looked too bad on camera but when Mike slowed it down to analyse me, it was a totally different story and a massive eye opener! On one side I landed heel first and on the other side I landed forefoot. I had a HUGE contralateral hip drop on the right side and a left arm that swung right out and across my body. My right foot crossed over the centre line and I clipped my right calf with my left foot. Was it any surprise that I had so many injuries! I was a typical example of a runner that got injured, carried on training, compensated and ended up with all sorts of funky movement patterns and don't even get me started on my functional movement test! I scored well below average which was a surprise to someone who trained hard and did plenty of strength work.

Instead of being discouraged by the analysis, I was excited that I had things to work on and the possibility of becoming a stronger, more efficient and most of all injury free runner! I went home full of enthusiasm and put it all into practice. It was hard and I really had to concentrate but my mind was fixed on developing a more efficient running form no matter how much effort it required initially.

The hardest part of the re-education process was getting my glutes to fire consistently, I had to repeat simple exercises over and over daily. I was convinced I'd never feel my glutes fire! I also found the leg cycle extremely tiring to maintain. Mike advised me to run for one minute and walk for one minute at the beginning. Of course, I thought I'd try and go for longer and I clearly remember having to sit down after four minutes because I was completely puffed out and thinking 'okay, he's right!' I decided then and there that I never wanted to run in my old style, and I didn't care if I could only run for one minute at a time, I'd build on it!

As I write this in 2021, I am proud and grateful to say that I have now being running for five years injury free and that's not bad for someone who runs 5-6 times per week! Both my glutes fire in sequence and I can maintain the leg cycle with no extra effort required. I've worked and continue to work extremely hard on specific strength work and run technique. If I start to feel a niggle developing, I know what to do to ensure that it doesn't end up as an injury which could stop me running.

Following the Functional Biomechanics of Running Course, I continued on to do the Certified Running Technique Specialist Course with The Running School and then opened my own Run Technique Centre near York (The Running & Movement Hub) so I could teach this to other runners who are fed up with being injured and want to improve the efficiency of their run technique.

I love running and the evolving journey it takes us on, and I can't thank Mike enough for helping me understand how to run injury free!

Mike: The first time I met Rachel, was at one of our two-day courses we run for therapists and coaches called Functional Biomechanics of Running.

She was bubbly and enthusiastic and was smiling continuously during day one of the course. She spoke to me a little nervously at the end of the first day: "This is the best course I have ever attended I have learnt so much already and I can't wait until tomorrow to learn more. Will you get a chance to analyse the video of my running technique tomorrow?"

The smile disappeared the next day when I went through the running and movement analysis. It was replaced by a frown and a massive look of disappointment. I had seen that look of deflation hundreds of times from runners who had had a number of different injuries over the years. Like many runners who get injured but keep on running through pain and discomfort. They go from one compensation to another and are truly surprised and overwhelmed when you breakdown their running movements.

Rachel wanted to learn how to run pain free and how to run faster and was determined to put in all the hard work into her training. We started working on Rachel's movement, re-educating her running technique and making sure we focused on her posterior chain weaknesses. It was hard for Rachel in the beginning because I was restricting her running to short intervals. Every time we reached a milestone she would try and run further and faster and have a small set-back. But she learnt very quickly.

She has a stubborn streak and a determination to improve as a runner and as a coach. She has become an excellent runner and an even better

Running and Rehabilitation Coach and is part of our network of Certified Running Technique Specialists. She has a wonderful personality who genuinely wants to help people. She is doing that daily, helping so many runners achieve their goals.

3
PROPRIOCEPTION
&
DYNAMIC MOVEMENT
SKILLS

What is Proprioception?

Proprioception is our sense of positioning and movement. It is our sixth sense.

Proprioception directs a continuous feedback and feedforward loop between our peripheral and central nervous system, the brain, and the sensory receptors in our body - in and around the joints, ligaments, muscles and skin. These receptor nerves measure our interaction with the ground, our speed of movement, our balance, weight shifting and send the message to the brain via the spinal cord and the cerebellum. The brain processes and interprets the message and sends back a signal to the body to react and make the necessary correction to produce the required movement.

In the time it has taken you to read this paragraph the brain and the somatosensory receptors have exchanged thousands of messages - not a slow process!

The processing of sensory information occurs at both conscious and unconscious levels. If everything is moving fluently then this is an automatic or unconscious process. We don't have to think about these messages or the corrections and adjustments to the movements.

Where pain is present, there is an interruption to the motor process – the pain begins to affect the complex muscle activation process and therefore the movement itself. The messaging from the receptors gets interrupted and the brain, to protect us, switches off different neuropathways which link to the body maps. This affects our motor control and our proprioceptive response and even when the pain has subsided, the sensation when you use that limb feels strange.

This can lead to movement dysfunction and interruption of the recruitment of the neuropathways, and this has a knock-on effect on the feedback of the proprioceptive system. This interruption affects synchronisation of movement and causes imbalances, poor coordination, and slower movement. It is also a major factor in the recurrence of injuries and sensory motor amnesia, where certain muscles fail to activate during movement and /or we can't feel them activating.

Have you ever gone over on your ankle or had pain in your calf and taken some time off running? Then when you start running again it does not feel like it is working with the rest of your body?

If you have had a joint, muscle or ligament injury, there will be a decrease in your proprioceptive ability. This can leave you susceptible to re-injuring the same body part but also, by compensating and overloading the opposite side, your ability to balance and coordinate movement gets disrupted and you get injured somewhere else.

The good news is that the proprioceptive system can be trained through specific exercises, and the motor unit re-educated and improved after the interruption due to injury.

The proprioceptive system has several important roles in the development of the motor process:

- It gives feedback for immediate adjustments and refinement of movement
- It gives feedback for motor learning

- It helps to develop and to re-enforce existing motor programmes
- It gives us synchronisation of muscles
- It enhances movement and balance and stability
- It improves incorrect and uncontrolled movement patterns

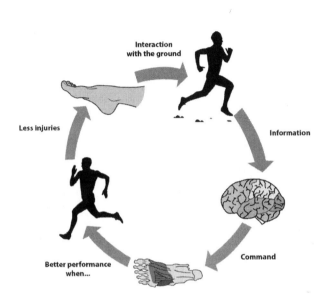

During extremely fast movements like running, jumping, kicking or playing a musical instrument quickly, the processing of the sensory messaging through the neuropathways is too slow to allow enough time to make the correction or refinement to the movement or muscle group. Therefore, the motor system must access and recruit the existing pre-programmed motor patterns, or motor engram, which precedes the sensory feedback. The motor system must rely on this map of the movement which has been created in the past, rather than react to the instant feedback from the movement.

Dynamic Movement Skills™ (DMS) is a rehabilitation and performance training methodology that we have developed. We use the protocols to stimulate and enhance the proprioceptive system and to improve the interaction with the ground. We also use the same methodology as part of our rehabilitation process.

This neuromuscular training method is based on biomechanical and sensorimotor control to achieve functional movement, dynamic joint stability, balance and control. The emphasis is on the quality of movement, correct movement control and working in all three movement planes: sagittal, frontal, and transverse. These skills ultimately help to increase our movement competency, and confidence in functional movement, running and sport.

Neuromuscular control is the trained, unconscious response of a muscle to a signal.

Neuromuscular exercise improves functional movement and performance. Simply doing strength exercises, without restoring neuromuscular control, is not enough for functional recovery of a joint or muscle because we must also restore the sensorimotor deficiencies and the movement map.

The DMS protocols have been developed to progress the patient or athlete through a series of movement patterns designed to correct the 'transmission' time and firing sequence within the central nervous system to correct movement patterns. It progresses from basic movement re-education to functional neuromotor stimulation, to dynamic movement development. They work through a series of movement patterns which challenge the proprioceptive system and the brain.

The movements start with short bursts of ten to twenty seconds of low impact, high quality and high intensity foot or hand placements. They progress to rapid acceleration, followed by rapid deceleration patterns of training, involving the usage of jumps, hops and skips.

This form of training, controlled by the stretch-shortening cycle, is also known as plyometrics.

Plyometric movements can be separated into two categories depending upon the duration of the ground contact time:

Fast plyometric movements of less than ($\leq$250 milliseconds) or 0.25 of one second and;

Slow plyometric activities of greater than ($\geq$251 milliseconds) or 0.251 seconds.

Dynamic Movement Skills training, takes advantage of the rapid muscle action known as the 'Stretch-shortening Cycle' (SSC), where the muscle undergoes an eccentric contraction, followed by an interim period preceding the concentric contraction. The combination of the speed of movement and the contraction of the muscle decreases, what is called, the amortisation time - the amount of time spent on the ground between the deceleration and acceleration of movement.

There are many neurophysiological benefits that reinforce this type of training which include:

- Improved storage and utilisation of elastic strain energy
- Improved active muscle working range
- Improved involuntary nervous reflexes
- Improved length-tension characteristics
- Increased muscle pre-activity

More importantly - greater motor coordination - which applies to, and benefits both athletes and rehabilitation patients.

We have been using Dynamic Movement Skills methodology and Plyometrics in our protocols for over twenty-five years with different cross-sections of the population.

With elite and recreational runners, we have found that by incorporating these exercises into their training programme, it improves their speed and Running Economy in a six-to-eight-week training block.

Dynamic resistance training and explosive training can increase the performance and speed for endurance and distance athletes by between 4% to 11%.

One of the components of Running Economy is the ability to use the stretch shortening cycle during ground contact. DMS training - which resembles low level plyometrics - enhances the muscle's ability to generate power, through stimulating the SSC. This improves the ability of the lower limb joints to react with the ground on contact between eccentric and concentric contractions.

What happens is that the nervous system adapts to the movement training to allow better intermuscular coordination of all the relevant muscles used, which leads to better proprioception and the runner's relationship with the ground when running, which leads to better motor unit activation to produce more force with less energy.

Hence better Running Economy.

To put it simply, we reduce the amount of time a runner spends on the ground. The less time we spend on the ground when running, the faster we run. Runners with greater reactive and elastic strength are more economical with every stride.

DMS training incorporates quick and accurate counter movement jumps, which help to improve reaction time of the lower limbs with the ground therefore producing 'Optimal Stiffness' which improves motor unit firing.

Another very important part of the Training Methodology is training single leg strength, balance, quickness and reactivity.

When we run, we spend 50% of our ground contact time on one leg. Through improving our single leg, hip and glute activation and reactive strength – which is different to leg strength – we can achieve better stride frequency and stride length without collapsing when the leg is fully weight bearing on the ground.

There are an increasing amount of studies supporting the use of resistance and dynamic training in distance running programmes.

We have included a series of DMS exercises in the Exercise Library and incorporated the movements in the training sessions for you to train your neuromuscular and proprioceptive systems.

HARRIET'S STORY

Harriet Millar-Mills
Wasps & England Rugby Player

I first went to The Running School six months after my 2nd ACL reconstruction and fifteen months after my initial knee injury. Only the week before I had restarted running with my physiotherapist, so if anything, I was sceptical as to why I needed to go since I was already running. In my mind I was looking to get back fit so I could potentially play some rugby sevens and get in shape for pre-season. Mike had other plans.

The first visit seemed pretty simple. I had been pre-warned that I would be warmed up then I would have my running technique analysed. Warming up at the Running School is very different to any warm-up I had done before! Starting with DMS to test my proprioception, (where you jump/step over a line as fast as you can), anyone who has done this will know the shock of being exhausted from twenty seconds of moving your feet. Safe to say I was not very good, neither physically nor cardio vascularly! Mike thoroughly analysed my running technique. I left exhausted and excited for the potential improvements he could make, along with a bruised ego, oh and homework, of walking forty minutes every day until my next session.

Learning how to walk properly is the most valuable skill I learnt in the first few weeks of training with Mike and his team. It affects everything we do and until I started to follow the cues he gave me, I had never realised my poor posture, the way I bounced when I walked and how my arms lacked any biomechanical influence.

Over the next few months I completed daily walks, weekly DMS and learnt how to jump onto boxes all over again. His team would tweak my movements each session, ensuring I was activating the correct muscles for each movement. This attention to detail is something that I had never experienced before, teaching me how to recognise it myself so I could complete the movements correctly at home.

The first day I was 'allowed' to run again, Mike had me walking backwards on a treadmill (surprisingly this is something I continue to do before most sessions for recovery after a game). I finished my sets thinking I was about to get off to do some jumps and he sprung it on me, "Now you get to run!"

Honestly, the fear and excitement were all rolled into one, I totally understand why he did not tell me until thirty seconds before. I still had to hold on to the handle to ensure my lower body was comfortable completing the correct technique, but still I was running on a treadmill, and this was a huge milestone!

Prior to joining The Running School, I had been injured for seventeen months - improving my mindset and regaining confidence in my knee seemed an insurmountable challenge. Once I was comfortable running, Mike effortlessly guided me through countless more milestones. I do not remember the first time I changed direction, the first-time wearing boots again, the first time looking at speed, but I do remember the realisation after doing sessions outside on the pitch at how far I had come. If anything, Mike celebrated these wins for me before I acknowledged it myself.

Mike endured working with me for nine months before I returned to play. The Running School being based at Wasps FC meant Mike could not stop me frequently popping my head in. We prepared for my first competitive match after being twenty-three months out. I was so excited about playing, and Mike's retort was "It'll take a few games to get yourself back into a competitive edge." was what I had come to expect from Mike. Characteristically direct, brutally honest and unfalteringly supportive.

When the knee injury returned to haunt me, there wasn't a moment's hesitation in contacting Mike. My surgeons estimated sixteen weeks rehabilitation. Mike got me back in nine. I continue to attend The Running School alongside playing for Wasps and England. I will never be able to put into words my gratitude to Mike and his team for all they have done for me. The simple truth is that: I don't think I would still be playing the sport I love, without them.

Mike: The Wasps Director of Rugby Giselle Mather had warned me and prepared me on Harriet's mindset. "She had had two ACL operations in fifteen months. We want her to come and see you and we want her back ready for the season. But she is sceptical and concerned after having a setback in her rehabilitation the first-time round. You have to convince her that this is where she should be." Harriet had been an England International since 2011 and had played in the 2017 world cup. She was a two-times Women's Premiership Players' Player of the Year. When she wasn't training or playing rugby competitively, she was a Maths Teacher.

She was used to getting injuries; they are part of the game, but this one tested her patience and affected her confidence. She was nervous when she first came to see me and, although very polite, made it clear with her posture that she did not really see how we could help her. I said that we would be evaluating her walking and running, as well as her movement to see if she had any compensations and then we would sit down and I would go through the videos and explain if and how we could help her.

Harriet had never had her walking and running biomechanics analysed and was intrigued at what we would find. She made a few excuses about her fitness level but was surprised at how her legs were behaving when we tested her proprioception and her interaction with the ground.

By the time we sat down to analyse the videos and go through her scores, her attitude had changed. She could see where her weaknesses were and was asking a lot of questions. She wanted to know what we would do. Why? What would be the outcome? I explained what we could do and the process that we would follow to help her get back to peak performance. I also cautioned that she would have to be patient and not hasten her rehab otherwise she would get re-injured.

I knew it was important to re-build Harriet's confidence through the training not just through words. After being injured for so long, it doesn't matter how strong you are mentally, there is always that feeling lingering in the background that you may never run again, may never play again, or even if you do, you will not be at the same level you were before.

We had to re-build Harriet's movement from the bottom upwards. Starting with her walking, then her running. It was important for her to understand what we already knew. We see a lot of ACL injuries in our centre every year. Re-injury rates following return to sport are quite high. Harriet had already been through two surgeries in seventeen months. Although there are many reasons why this happens, one of the frequently identified factors is the failure to retrain motor control and running biomechanics, which results in compensations and irregular movement.

Over the following months, Harriet progressed to running, sprinting and rugby contact again. In her first game back after the injury, I was more nervous than she was! It was like watching one of my own children play for the first time. She is back playing for England again, has just been part of the team that won the six nations and is preparing to go to a world cup. We continue to see her regularly for speed sessions and the occasional rehab.

4
RUNNING TECHNIQUE:
OUR PHILOSOPHY

Running is a skill and just like any other skill it can be taught, it can be developed, and it can be improved through a systematic and progressive training approach.

Many people believe that your running technique, or your 'form', as some like to call it, is something you are born with and you can't really change it. Among them are many sport coaches at both elite and youth level.

When I first started studying the way athletes run, it was following two serious injuries which kept me out of playing football for nine months, when I was sixteen. We used to train in a stadium which had a dirt running track around the pitch. I used to spend hours after school jogging around the track and pounding the stadium stairs and then stretching during my prescribed rehab. I used to watch the athletes come into train and compare them to the footballers. I admired their seemingly effortless long strides. I asked my coach "How can I run like that?" His answer was "You can't, that's why they are athletes, and you are a footballer."

Years later when I began coaching, I found out for myself that he was more than a little wrong.

One of the issues with many Sports Clubs, Running Clubs and Athletic Clubs is that there is no effective teaching of running biomechanics. In running, most coaches coach what they experienced during the time they were athletes. The focus is on the volume of training, the weekly mileage, and the intensity of the training sessions. Little time, if any at all, is dedicated to teaching running technique and correcting biomechanical inefficiencies. Sometimes this is a time issue and sometimes this is due to lack of knowledge.

This is not just the case at amateur and recreational level. Having worked with elite and professional athletes from different sports and disciplines over the past thirty years, the lack of biomechanical coaching is obvious.

There are many ways of approaching the structure of running training. But even today - with all the modern coaching methodologies, technology, available knowledge, and research - running training is coached as just conditioning fitness and, in many cases, it is counterproductive to the improvement of the athlete, particularly after injury.

In many professional sports and particularly in their academies, no consideration is given to individual running technique, the relationship between functional movement, the neuromuscular system, the type of speed required for their sport, and the injuries that they get.

We believe everyone has their own unique 'running movement patterns'. Everyone moves in a unique way. The way they run affects how they land, how long they spend on the ground and how the different loading forces affect different muscles and joints.

Most runners haven't been taught how to run efficiently. They just run.

Running is a life skill and I believe that along with walking, it should be taught in primary schools and secondary schools as part of the curriculum. We should start from the age of seven when we get control of our body and repeat it again through puberty and adulthood.

We have a passion for working with children and teaching them efficient movement, running technique and speed. A third of all the people we coach in the UK are children under the age of fourteen. They learn from us, and we learn from them. But we would need another volume to include the methodology for coaching & teaching movement to children!

Walking and running are our primary and secondary gaits. These two movement patterns are what we use for seventy to eighty years of our life.

Yet we spend little time perfecting the skills that could keep us healthy, increase our longevity and keep us mobile when we get older. Thus, improving our quality of life into old age; especially after injury or illness.

One of the questions I get asked many times is whether I get frustrated when I see runners running with an inefficient technique. Do I feel the urge to go up to people and explain they are running badly?

They are surprised when I say **"No, absolutely not!"**

Running is about how you feel - what it does for you personally. Most people who run do so to keep their fitness up, to destress or just to feel good. They may not participate in races and are not interested in posting their time on Strava or other social media sites. They just want to run because of how it makes them feel!

About twenty years ago, I was on my way home in the evening from coaching. Our centre at the time, was located in the London Underground arches in Chiswick. In the spring and summer, I used to see this runner 2-3 times a week running up and down the long street at about the same time in the evening. He had an interesting running style: he didn't use his arms and he would run almost bent over from the waist as if he were about to fall. It looked particularly stressful.

Many times, as I drove passed him, I said to myself "I should stop and talk to him. I can help him to run better and faster, and he will enjoy his running a lot more." On this particular day, I had just finished working with two elite track athletes who were going to the Olympics and we had a great training session. I was on a coaching high!

I saw the runner again stumbling along. So, I parked the car ahead of him, got out and as he came towards me, I held out my hand and said "Hi, I'm a running coach and I have seen you run along here many times. I can help you to run better and faster."

He slowed down to a walk, sidestepped me, and said bluntly – "F*** Off!"

Lesson learnt. Red-faced, I quickly got back in the car and drove off. Never did it again.

He was right of course. I didn't know him or know anything about him or why he runs, or if he wanted to change his running. We help thousands of people every year with their running to become better runners, to overcome injuries and to get faster and participate in races. We coach children to be more coordinated, to get control of their body and to get fast. Everyone has their own reason for running.

But that doesn't mean that everyone who runs should or will want to change their running technique! So, I want to emphasise the following:

- It doesn't matter what you look like when you run
- It doesn't matter how fast you run
- It doesn't matter if you plod along and you don't look good
- It doesn't matter if you only run-walk
- It doesn't matter if you only run short distances
- It doesn't matter if you don't participate in races
- It doesn't matter if you are not wearing all the latest gear
- It doesn't matter if you don't have the best trainers

WHAT MATTERS IS HOW YOU FEEL!

As long as you are enjoying it and it makes you feel good, keep doing what you're doing!

If, however you want to improve your running and run faster, or you are getting running related injuries, or are new to running and want to learn the skill, keep reading.

If you finish a run and feel like you have just been in the ring with a wrestler, for example…

- Your calves are so tight you cannot walk correctly
- You have pain in the knees
- You have pain in the shins
- Your quadriceps are stiff and sore
- Your hip flexors are so tight that you are leaning forward
- Your shoulders are tight and painful
- You have back pain
- Your hamstrings feel so tight you can't bend over

...then it's time to fix the issues!

Many runners compensate in different ways and when we start getting injuries, we want to find quick solutions. We then begin to look for answers and inevitably end up doing searches on the internet.

You think to yourself "I will just google that. I am sure thousands more runners must have experienced this, there should be a quick and easy solution." and then you find that you are bombarded with a wide-ranging list of what could be causing your problem.

Top of the list and the most common thing to recommend for a change, are the trainers. We then go through the process of investigating shoes. Looking at what everyone else is wearing to get faster, and to avoid injuries, and we start to ask questions to anyone who will listen:

- Is it the thickness of the sole?
- Should I wear a shoe with a thinner sole or thicker sole?
- Is it the type of shoe?
- Are my shoes too narrow, too wide?
- Are the shoes too old?
- Will new shoes sort out my injury?
- Do I need to buy more expensive shoes?
- These are not my favourite colour. Maybe that's what it is?
- The nice person in the shop said I need insoles with the new trainers.
- Maybe I need orthotics?

After we purchase two or three different types of shoes, because we are not sure which one will solve the problem, and with the same injuries persisting, the research extends to other reasons:

- Is it flexibility and lack of stretching? But I stretch and do Yoga or Pilates.
- Is it a strength issue? Am I weak?
- Do I need to go to a gym? But I'm a runner I hate the gym!
- Is it mobility? Is that why my hips are tight?
- I will buy a foam roller. I have seen them advertised.
- Maybe if I buy compression socks that will sort out the problem?

- I will also buy some knee compression sleeves.
- Maybe I need orthotics.

Then in desperation we decide to visit a therapist:

- My therapist said it's because my glutes don't work
- My therapist said I have tight hamstrings I need to stretch more
- My therapist said my core doesn't function
- My therapist said all my problems are because of my foot strike
- If I change to forefoot strike, I will be Ok
- My therapist said I need minimalist shoes
- My therapist said all my problems are because my cadence is too slow, I need to run at 180 steps per minute

Because information is at our fingertips, we want to find quick, and of course easy solutions to our running issues and particularly our injuries.

There are many 'experts' promoting their services on the internet, with varying degrees of knowledge. From good, experienced runners, to physiotherapists and sports therapists, strength specialists, running magazines and many online coaches.

As humans we have a tendency to gravitate towards the answer that we most want to hear. We want information that matches and supports our beliefs at that time.

So, if someone is making a persuasive argument that resonates with what we want to hear or supports our belief, then this increases the dopamine in the brain. The more we see things that re-enforce our beliefs, the more it changes how we see or hear the issues or the problems.

Rather than get more deeply into the rights and wrongs of social media information and how it influences our beliefs and the decisions we make. We will stick to running!

Okay two things to clarify here: i) This may surprise you but… not everything on the internet is correct and true! ii) Running Technique is not just about the way your foot lands, the shoes you wear or your cadence.

Let's first explore what running technique IS NOT and bust a few of the most common myths at the same time.

What Running Technique IS NOT

It isn't just about foot strike. Do you choose heel, forefoot or midfoot landing? Just changing your foot strike to land forefoot is not changing your running technique, it is transferring the forces to a different part of the body. It can take up to twelve months to transition from heel strike to forefoot landing in order to avoid injury. Forefoot landing is not for everyone. Foot strike has been a hot subject for many years now and we will discuss in more detail further in this chapter.

It isn't just about the shoes. It's the runner that runs not the shoes. The shoes make a difference in your comfort if you pick the right one for you. They can cause you a lot of discomfort if you pick the wrong size or fit. Some new trainers with plate technology will give you between 2% - 4% advantage in running speed. Which can make a big difference if you are an elite athlete. But the shoes do not do the running for you. Yes, the shoes are important, but they will not make you faster or protect you from injury if you are not fit and have not trained correctly.

It isn't just about cadence. 180 steps per minute, the magical number put forward by some coaches, many therapists and online running gurus as the answer to running technique, injury prevention and running efficiency! Should you worry about your cadence not being 180 steps per minute? No, it's just one small part of running we explain this further below.

What Running Technique IS

It is, first and foremost, about movement patterns. Your body learns through movement; if you practice correct movement, the body learns correct movement.

If you practice an inefficient movement, your brain and your body will learn an inefficient movement and as soon as you try to increase the volume of training or the intensity of the training, because of the inefficient movement, your body starts to complain and injuries occur.

Running Technique is about the whole body, the way the arms move affects your balance and determines the level of forward momentum and stride length.

Dynamic core strength and the way you use your torso plays a huge role on how much time you spend on the ground and the amount of force that travels through the ankle, knee, hip and back.

The way your legs and the arms move determines your stride frequency, stride length and the amount of force with which you hit the ground. The way your feet land can determine how efficient you become in transitioning from one foot to another, how much you 'break' when you land and how much force goes through each stride.

Let's Talk More About Cadence

Cadence is the number of steps you take per minute. You measure it by counting the number of steps you take in sixty seconds, just on one leg and then multiply by two. There are also several GPS watches and foot sensors that you can attach to your shoe that will measure it for you.

So now you have your cadence number, or your steps per minute number, what does it tell you and is it important?

This is your running rhythm at a certain speed. If you want to run faster, then the two elements you need to improve are: i) Your stride length and ii) your stride frequency; these two are inextricably linked.

Stride length is the distance that you travel over the ground when running. It is measured one leg at a time. You stride length is measured from the toe of the right leg as it leaves the ground, to the toe or heel of the left leg as it touches the ground.

Your height, weight, age, fitness, speed and very importantly running experience, all influence your running.

Cadence is determined by how fast you run and your stride length. It is also linked to how tall you are and how much contact time you have with the ground.

Because everyone is different, there is a big variation in cadence between individual runners, and specifically beginner runners, depending on their speed. If you are jogging or running at slower speeds, your cadence will be slower. A runner's cadence could vary from 140 to 210 Steps Per Minute, depending on the speed and the distance they run.

Crucially, there is no magic cadence number that you need to achieve to become a more efficient runner.

Increasing your running speed will increase your cadence. Increasing your cadence will not necessarily increase your speed.

If you increase your cadence but are still running at a slow speed, then all you are doing is shortening you stride length and making more contact with the ground. If your running technique is not efficient then you will get injured.

Another interesting fact is that taller runners have longer strides, and therefore have a lower cadence than shorter runners because they have longer legs. In a recent study on stride frequency, it showed that someone who is 6 ft (180CM) tall would run eighteen steps per minute less than someone who is 5.6 ft (168CM).

Simply increasing your cadence by 5-10%, as some suggest, is not the answer to better running technique or better running efficiency or injury prevention.

Why, you may ask, are so many so called 'experts' so fixated on cadence if it's only of secondary importance? Where has this loud opinion come from?

Cadence has been a heated theme in running conversations for some time, particularly since social media became active on the internet. Many refer to the observations that Jack Daniels made during the 1984 Olympics. Sitting in the stands observing track qualifiers in middle distance to long distance races, he counted their steps. He noted that of the fifty or so athletes he studied, all were running with a cadence **of greater** than 180 steps per minute.

It seems that this information was taken as a 'law of running' and the information was misinterpreted or taken out of context. He also reported that the 800M and 1500M athletes were running more than 200 steps per minute.

Looking simply at the rule of 180 SPM, ignores a few key facts:

- The athletes were running at a rate greater than 180 SPM
- The runners were running at speeds faster than 18 KMH
- The speed of the runner determines the cadence
- Every runner is different

As regards the reason why so many experts are fixated with running cadence of 180? My view is that it is an easy instruction to give a runner. It is easier to say "All you need to do is increase you cadence to 180 SPM" rather than explain the biomechanical issues involved with improving running technique, increasing stride length or reducing ground contact time, or improving cardiovascular capacity.

Other Considerations

There are other important factors to take into consideration and focus on if you want to become a better runner.

Running mechanics, aerobic fitness, endurance, maintaining speed and the way that you train, to name a few.

Running experience and the way that you train plays an exceptionally significant role in optimising your individual running pace. There is a difference between beginner and recreational runners and experienced or elite runners - who have had more time and training sessions to develop and optimise their running over the years.

One of the key characteristics of elite runners, is they have less contact time with the ground. Less contact time with the ground means they are moving faster over the ground and have fewer breaking forces going through the legs.

This is because they have better running efficiency, they overstride less, they have better cardiovascular ability, they can maintain their speed for longer and can manage their pace and optimise their stride.

When we train elite and recreational athletes, cadence is not a variable we measure. Improved cadence comes with improvements in running technique and running speed. Elite runners do not focus on cadence when they are training or competing. The training focus is on technique, endurance, strength and speed.

If you want to become a better, faster runner, the emphasis should not be on increasing your cadence. The attention should be on first improving your running technique, followed by specific training sessions that increase your endurance, strength and speed.

These sessions should include, running shorter, faster, interval training sessions at 200M and 400M. Followed by 800M and 1KM repetitions and hill repeat sessions.

The table below shows the different speeds and cadence values at a pace per KM so you can get an idea of how different running speeds affect cadence.

PACE Min/Km	Speed KPH	Cadence
3:00	20	200+
3:35	17	190
4:38	13	173
5:00	12	165
6:00	10	160
7:30	8	140

Trainers

In the last twenty years, the running industry and particularly the shoe and clothing sectors, have undergone a huge change because of the improvement in expertise, technology and the materials used for manufacturing.

The marketing messages were primarily targeted at injury prevention and speed. The slogans were bold, inspirational, with a touch of arrogance and designed to influence runners into buying their shoes.

The 'barefoot' revolution – which is really an oxymoron as most people don't run barefoot - began to change the way runners looked at foot strike and running technique.

We have experienced the minimalist period, which influenced runners to ditch their thick soled trainers and purchase minimalist shoes and convert to forefoot running. The marketing message was strong and effective, and millions of pairs of shoes were sold. Still runners got the same injuries.

In early 2011, I received a phone call from an elite triathlete.

"Mike, I need to come and see you to improve my running speed, but I am just recovering from an injury, so I will give you a call in a couple of weeks."

He called me again about a month later and relayed the same story. I said:

"Why, don't you come in and we can have a look at the injury and see if we can help?"

He eventually came in for biomechanical analysis 3 months after the original injury in December. I asked him to walk on the treadmill and found that he was limping badly and both his Achilles tendons were inflamed. As we could not analyse his running, I asked one of our physiotherapists to assess the injury while we chatted.

"So how did the injury happen?"

"My wife bought me the book "Born to Run" (by Christopher McDougall) for Christmas. Do you know it?"

"Yes, I have read it"

"I got so excited by the story that I went out and bought some minimalist trainers and ran a 10K the next day, landing forefoot. My calves blew up and I couldn't walk for a few days, so I did some swimming and some turbo training and I felt better after a week. Then I decided to try the new shoes again. I went for another 10K run and this time I could not walk for a couple of weeks, so I rested and just did some swimming and gentle cycling. But that didn't help. I had some massage but that didn't help either and here I am."

The triathlete, who is a big guy with big feet, suddenly went from heel striking (as he had all his life) to forefoot with the new trainers – all because he wanted to run faster. But by changing only his foot strike, rather than his actual technique, he overloaded his lower limb. We referred him to a specialist. He was not able to run for 12 months. We helped him with his rehabilitation and then re-educated his running technique. This wasn't an isolated incident. It happens often when runners switch to minimalist trainers.

When we had the 'pronation' is wrong and can cause injuries argument, more technological innovation was used to create motion control shoes. If you went to buy trainers and the shop assistant deemed that you were a 'pronator' or a 'supinator', then you were sold shoes that would 'correct the problem.' Still runners got the same injuries.

When you go into a sports store to get your gait analysed to try on new trainers. Most shops will only analyse from the knee down to the foot. They don't look at full body biomechanics. But as you will see later in the movement patterns section, how the arms move can affect how the feet land and how much we break and if our legs cross-over the midline. Which can also affect how our feet strike the ground.

We have had shoe companies removing the heel from their shoes, adding an extra inch on the forefoot part of the shoe, hiking up the price and marketing it to athletes as the new revolution in running. Many triathletes were shocked when we analysed them and showed them that in fact, they were still striking the ground with the heel first. "But I paid a lot of money for these trainers to stop me from landing heel first!"

Recently we have had a resurgence of thick soled trainers again and runners are hailing the 'new' shoe technology as the answer to their injury woes.

The challenge that runners have, with all this conflicting information is to identify what is the best shoe for them. As a runner you must try to find the right trainers for you. The process is one of trial and error.

At the time of writing, there is no definitive solution to the perfectly fitting shoe for every individual.

I believe that every runner has their own unique 'movement patterns'. Therefore, that will also translate to the forces that go through the foot, the ankle joint, the shin, the calf, the tendons, the knee, the hip and lower back when they run. They are unique to every individual.

So, while we wait for the day when we can walk into the sport shop of the future, where we can run on a 3D treadmill that can measure the exact size of our feet and how they react to our body load when we run. Calculate the correct size, the required comfort level for recreational running and for performance running. Based on the distance that we run and how much we train. Where the artificial intelligence will measure the various forces that go through the joints and muscles and then produce a pair of shoes that is specifically and uniquely designed and developed for each individual runner!

Until that time comes, and if you haven't got any medical or structural issues, here is the advice we offer:

Try on a variety of trainers that are the correct size, width and are appropriate for you to run on the terrain you most frequently run on. Pick a neutral shoe, without any 'motion control' and run with them before you buy them. If they are not comfortable in the store, they will not be comfortable when you go for a run outside. As for the colour of the trainers, which we know is especially important, select this after you have found the right trainers. It's not very scientific but it is simple, and it works most of the time.

Foot strike

There have been several arguments put forward by running experts and physical therapists who support 'barefoot' or minimalist footwear principles. About how our foot should strike the ground when we are running. The most vociferous argument, is that the only way to land when your foot strikes the ground when running, is 'forefoot'.

The reasoning behind this according to those who recommend it: "It's the natural way to land when running." and "Because all elite athletes land this way." This is also supported by advocates of not getting injured and running faster.

Therefore, a lot of the advice given to recreational runners has been, and by the way still is, to change their foot strike if they are a heel striker, to forefoot or midfoot. The claim put forward is that all elite middle distance and long-distance runners do not land on their heels, therefore, if elite athletes run like that, so should everyone else.

The conclusion that many runners derive from the information they read or are offered, is that everyone who runs whatever the distance, needs to change their foot strike to forefoot running, and their cadence to 180 SPM. This will ensure that runners reduce injuries and maximize performance.

This is quite a widespread claim amongst many runners, coaches and therapists and, to be frank, it is wrong.

The data and the evidence do not support these claims.

When Nike was developing their special shoe for the sub two-hour marathon attempt, they also produced a prototype with no heel. Great idea… in theory! The problem was, they had not consulted the athletes who were going to run. The athletes disliked it and refused to run in it. Kipchoge, who is predominantly a midfoot striker, lands differently depending on the surface that he runs on, and the shoes that he wears. His team of runners assembled for the attempt found it very strange to not have a heel on the shoe. Even if they land forefoot, in midstance they always put their heel down. The 'Vaporfly Elite' was the shoe they ended up with, which has a heavily cushioned heel with the famous carbon fiber plates to assist propulsion.

On the 12th October 2019, Kipchoge, described as 'the greatest marathon runner of all time', became the first runner in history to break the two-hour barrier in the marathon distance in a time of 1:59:40.

In 2020 because of the Covid-19 pandemic, all the big city Marathon races and competitions were cancelled. In October of 2020, the London Marathon organising committee decided to hold only the Elite Marathon race, which normally happens in April. This was run in a closed loop in a big park without spectators.

In the men's race, Shura Kitata of Ethiopia beat Sisay Lemma who came in second, in a time of 2:05:41. Shura Kitata, ran the whole race heel striking at an average speed of 20.2KM per hour or 12.5 miles per hour.

Eliud Kipchoge the current world record holder in the marathon, with a time of 2:01:39, finished in sixth place. He didn't have a good day, in the cold and the rain, and came in with a time of 2:06:49.

IAAF world Championships London 2017

At the 2017 world Championships in London, The IAAF commissioned a series of in-depth biomechanical analysis of all the races and competitions. They set-up high speed cameras in the stadium and along the marathon route and used different analysis software to collate the results.

The men's and women's marathon races produced some interesting data.

As with all major championships and Olympic games this was contested by the best male and female marathon runners in the world.

The study was not specifically set up to look at foot strike, but a number of different running variables including: Running speed, step length, step rate, ground contact time, flight time, foot-strike, as well as the various angles in the ankle, knee, hip, elbow and shoulder when running.

IAAF Men's Marathon London 2017

In the men's marathon, of the 70 finishers, forty-seven runners that is 67% of the field, landed on their heels. This included six out of the top eight athletes. Twenty-one runners, 30% landed on their midfoot. Two runners 2% of the field landed forefoot. The top four finishers were all heel strikers throughout the race. The speed of the top eight runners throughout the race ranged from 17Km to 19.69Km per hour.

Name	Time	Country	Foot strike
Geoffrey Kipkorir Kirui	2:09:49	KEN	Heel
Tamirat Tola	2:09:51	ETH	Heel
Alphonce Felix Simbu	2:10:17	Tan	Heel
Callum Hawkins	2:10:17	GBR	Heel
Gideon Kipkemoi Kipketer	2:10:56	KEN	Midfoot
Daniele Meucci	2:10:56	ITA	Midfoot
Yohanes Ghebregerois	2:12:07	ERI	Heel & Midfoot
Daniel Wanjiru	2:12:16	KEN	Heel & Midfoot

IAAF Women's Marathon London 2017

The results were similar in the women's marathon. There were seventy-eight female runners. Of those competing, fifty-seven runners or 73% landed heel first. Nineteen runners or 24% of the total field landed midfoot and two runners or 3% of the field landed forefoot.

Name	Time	Country	Foot strike
Rose Chelimo	2:27:11	BRN	Heel
Edna Ngeringwony Kiplagat	2:27:18	KEN	Forefoot
Amy Cragg	2:27:18	USA	Midfoot
Flomena Cheyech Daniel	2:27:21	KEN	Heel
Shure Demise	2:27:58	ETH	Heel on one foot Midfoot on the other
Eunice Jepkirui Kirwa	2:28:17	BRN	Heel
Hetah Jelagat Kiprop	2:28:19	KEN	Midfoot
Mare Dibaba	2:29:32	ETH	Heel

Let's be clear here. This doesn't mean that we now need to teach everyone to be a heel striker for longer distances!

There is no one rule that fits all runners. Besides the fact that runners come in all shapes and sizes, they also come in different age groups. If people discover running in their 40s, 50s or 60s they will have different movement patterns and different levels of fitness, different cardiovascular abilities and different strength levels. They will need time and practice to adjust to the forces that get generated when running. This is another area where improved running technique helps with longevity.

When we teach children how to run, we teach them how to adjust their running to forefoot and midfoot and heel strike depending on what sport there are doing, how fast they are running and their physical ability.

When we analyse distance runners from around the world, we see that when it comes to longer races, even with elite athletes, fatigue can cause changes to their running technique and this in turn can cause asymmetries in stride length, stride frequency, foot strike and overstride.

Some runners will start the race running forefoot and end up running heel first by the end of the race. Some will start as heel strikers and end up forefoot or midfoot.

Some runners will also be running one foot forefoot and one foot heel strike when they get tired or have pain!

Fatigue causes compensations in several areas. It is a key factor in identifying asymmetries and irregularities with the kinetic chain. The question is how this affects different individuals in a race or training. Elite runners have a better foundation in running and they spend less time in contact with the ground and are able to cope better with the forces that travel up the body.

Now that we have established the facts, the big question is what do we do about it? What can we change? What do we coach?

Everyone is different. No two runners are the same, but the human body works in the same way for each runner.

Running biomechanics is one part of running technique. It plays an important role in running efficiency. If you are running with good mechanics, you will spend less time on the ground, you will inevitably move faster over the ground. And run faster. You will also strike the ground with less body force and that reduces the number of injuries that you may get.

But there are other factors that need to be taken into consideration.

1. Left to right asymmetries in both legs and arms
2. Previous injury and compensation
3. Cardiovascular ability and stamina
4. Mobility and functional movement

5. Functional strength
6. The type of training that you do

Elite Runners

When we work with and study elite runners, we see a few key running characteristics which are common across male and female runners.

Starting from the bottom moving upwards

a. They have a distinct leg cycle. After toe-off, the heel comes up mid-way to the thigh or higher to the butt, the faster they run.

b. They can strike the ground in any one of three ways - midfoot, heel-toe or forefoot, depending on what surface they are running on and the distance they are running. On the track, if they are wearing racing flats, they will tend to land forefoot or mid-foot.

c. When they land the knee is slightly flexed.

d. The arms are moving in rhythm – they are all slightly different from runner to runner, but they move in synchronisation with the legs. The elbows are bent at less than 60 degrees for longer distances and at about 90 degrees for the sprints. The arms drive backwards to propel our body forwards and then come forward to chest or shoulder level.

e. The body is upright and not leaning too far forward.

f. The shoulders are not over-rotating on the axis and are driven by the arms.

g. They have an elasticity and an efficiency when they run.

If you are wondering how you can improve your running, and how much of this is natural - that is you are genetically blessed - and how much of this is down to hard work and training. Read on!

The Running School Method

Our **methodology** has been developed over thirty years to teach people how to use their body more efficiently when running, to reduce the risk of injury and to run faster. We treat everyone as an individual and give everyone access to the quality of coaching and resources that are usually reserved for elite athletes.

The Running School™ Three Key Steps.

1. MOVE BETTER

Whether the individual is a beginner, an elite runner or someone who is returning from injury, it is likely they are not moving as well as they need to be or can improve their movement and running efficiency. One of the first things we do is a detailed Biomechanical Analysis and Functional Movement Analysis. Through this we identify any weaknesses and movement issues. We believe that if someone is not moving efficiently that they will not be able to run efficiently.

2. RUN BETTER

Where we start, regardless of the individual's level, is by re-educating running technique and changing their individual movement patterns. We do this through our coaching methodology and training methods, to help runners achieve their goals.

3. RUN FASTER

Once we have improved an individual's technique and movement efficiency then we can work on improving their speed. This is based on their objectives, event, and of course this is dependent on the time and commitment that they can allocate to their training, strength, and recovery. We have developed several different speed protocols which we have used successfully with both amateur and professional athletes.

Why do so many runners get injured?

Depending on which research study you read, and there have been many over the last five years, every year between 56% and 90% of runners will sustain an injury that will require them to take a significant time off from running or to seek assistance from a medical practitioner.

When discussing running injuries, it is important to recognise that there are two different types of injuries. Acute or trauma injuries which happen, but are rare in running, and injuries due to repetitive loads being applied repeatedly over many runs.

Most of the injuries that runners get develop through inefficient running technique or due to landing shock.

Many of the running injuries are recurring and, even when the symptoms and the pain have gone away, as soon as the runners restart running the same problem arises again.

Beginner runners, often spend more time on the ground due to lack of technique, less elasticity, slow running speed, inefficient proprioception, or muscle activation issues. These factors, along with excessive breaking forces, mean that these stresses are repeated as you take each stride forward.

The human body and particularly the human foot is designed to absorb huge contact forces every day when we walk or run. That is hundreds of kilograms, as our foot comes into contact with the ground repeatedly, and the ground reaction forces push back to propel us forward.

If you are a runner who goes out for a run two to three times a week, the body can cope with the load, recover, and regenerate in a couple of days and over time, get used to the distance you run. Why then is running so hard on the body?

Running is stressful on the body. But that stress, or load, can increase due to incorrect running biomechanics. The injury risk is further increased as the runner increases the volume of running, by running longer distances too quickly, or the intensity of the running, by running more frequently or trying to run faster without being fit enough or having enough recovery.

When we run, we can put forces equal to between three to five times our body weight through every step. Starting with our foot and moving upwards to the knee and hip. The weight ratio depends on how long we spend on the ground, how hard we hit the ground and in which direction the forces are being directed.

As well as the forces that go through every single one of our steps when we run, the braking forces caused by inefficient biomechanics on foot strike add to the load.

In multidirectional sport like football, rugby, hockey etc., we also have the forces generated through deceleration, acceleration and change of direction.

It is important to remember that running is a single leg activity, so we are first on the left leg and then on the right leg when running, and in between we are in flight mode. The stress is absorbed by our tendons, muscles, cartilage, bones and ligaments with every single stride we take.

Let's look at an example of a recreational runner, Tim who we have coached. Tim runs three times per week and a longer run on the weekend. He runs about five hours per week and has a stride frequency of about 150 strides per minute. This is based on his average speed per kilometer or miles per hour, which is 10 KM per hour.

If Tim runs 5 hours per week and takes 75 strides per minute on each leg he will take:

- 150 strides per minute X 60 minutes = 9,000 steps per hour
- 9,000 steps in 60 minutes X 5 hours per week = 45,000 steps per week

Someone who runs:

- 6 hours per week can take 54,000 steps per week
- 8 hours per week can take 72,000 steps per week
- 10 hours per week can take 90,000 steps per week

A marathon takes between 40,000 to 46,000 steps to complete, so someone who is training for five hours per week is doing more than the equivalent of a marathon per week.

Tim is six foot tall or 180cm and weighs 85 kg. If he overstrides, he could be generating forces between 255 kg and 425 kg between three and five times his body weight, with every step he runs. This means during a 60-minute run, he could be putting his lower limbs through a lot of stress.

Over the course of a month, that is a lot of weight going through the body, if we are not running efficiently.

Now if we consider that many of us are running with inefficient movement patterns, then over the course of a month we could be taking over 250,000 inefficient steps. Well at some point our body will begin to complain!

This is what we call an overuse injury. Slower runners spend more time on the ground and therefore put more force and more bodyweight through their lower limbs. Novice runners especially, but also unfit runners, have a tendency to have a longer contact time with the ground, which affects the knee joint position and the coordination of the hip and ankle motion.

When Tim completed his running technique re-education, he improved his average speed by 1.5Km per hour and his cadence increased to over 160 SPM. In eight weeks, his 5K time improved by three minutes, his 10K time improved by eight minutes.

The chart below will give you an indication on how your pace affects your cadence and more importantly the speed you need to be running at to achieve your objectives. You can see how your cadence increases dynamically as the speed of your running increases.

Your target should be to increase your speed and your endurance to be able to sustain the pace for the desired distance. The increase in cadence is a byproduct. The stride length and the stride frequency will adjust depending on the pace at which you are comfortable or able to run.

If your pace is six minutes per kilometer then you are averaging a speed of 10KM per hour. If you were able to maintain that speed over a 5K then you would finish in thirty minutes and a 10K in approximately sixty minutes.

When recreational runners start to run consistently and want to challenge themselves they, inevitably, want to run longer distances. But if you are running a thirty minute 5K today, it does not mean you can automatically multiply your 5K time by the distance that you want to achieve.

This is one of the most common mistakes runners make. "Oh, I have been running 5K in thirty minutes therefore my half marathon time will be just over two hours and my marathon time will be around four hours."

The shorter distance time does not translate into the longer distance time by doing a quick multiplication. But by improving your ability to run at a certain pace for a certain time through training, you can achieve your goal.

Besides better running technique, there are four key training elements that you will need to improve on if want to run longer distances and avoid injury.

- Aerobic endurance which is your ability to continually run without tiring and the ability of the heart and lungs to cope with the distance
- Speed endurance, the ability to maintain the required running speed for the distance
- Functional strength for both upper and lower body and your core
- Mobility, to be able to have full range of motion in your muscles and joints

We have included examples of these different training sessions in the exercise library.

The table below provides a sample of some of the more popular distances and target times. The pace in minutes per KM and the average speed in KM per hour, required to achieve a certain time.

Pace Speed Race Performances Table with Cadence values

PACE Min/Km	Speed KPH	5K	10K	21K	42.2K	Cadence
3:00	20	15:00	30:00	1:03	2:06	200+
3:35	17	17:53	35:46	1:15	2:31	190
4:38	13	23:10	46:20	1:38	3:16	173
5:00	12	25:00	50:00	1:45	3:31	165
6:00	10	30:00	01:00	2:06	4:13	160
7:30	8	37:23	01:15	2:34	5:08	140

JUDY'S STORY

Judy Lewis
Cancer Survivor and Absolute Inspiration to all of us

In the spring of 2017, my Head & Neck Surgeon and Consultant at UCLH, Mr. Nicholas Kalavrezos (hereafter known as Mr. K), read me the 'riot act'. He was equally exasperated and proud by my determination to run the Virgin London Marathon. I had a charity place and I wanted to raise as much money as I could, as my way of saying thanks to the NHS for saving my life. Back in 2010, I had a rare and aggressive cancerous tumour (Spindle Cell Sarcoma) in my lower jaw. Mr. K and his team performed two major life saving procedures on me; to remove the tumour and most of my lower jaw, then reconstruct a new jaw, by grafting my fibula bones onto a titanium plate.

Cancer treatment was brutal, both psychologically and physically. I had to learn to walk, talk and eat again twice. I had extensive scarring on my legs and neck, along with facial disfigurement. The other significant issue I had, was that I developed a condition called Chronic Regional Pain Syndrome (CRPS) in my right foot and ankle. It was a complication from my first major surgery. In a nutshell, I have pain and a tingling sensation all the time, along with numbness and hypersensitivity, which means that I don't have a true feeling of what my foot is doing, especially when I'm running. This is why, it was so important that I found a specialist in the field to help me.

I don't have prosthetics in either of my lower legs, where my fibulas once were, I just have my tibias. Hence Mr. K's great concern about my newfound love of long-distance running. He basically said in as many words; "I don't know what to do with you. None of my patients have ever done anything like this before. You're going to have to see a sports specialist, to make sure that you're running properly, because you have only got your tibias." Many years later, Mr. K told me, that he was unsure if I'd even be able to walk at all following the second major surgery I needed.

So, to bring it back to meeting Mike, it was serendipity. At about the same time Mr. K instructed me to find a movement specialist, I was reading Vassos Alexander's book 'Don't Stop Me Now'. He talked about going to The Movement and Running School (TMRS), how Vassos had heard about

Mike and went to TMRS to improve his gait and running technique and described at length about how fantastic Mike Antoniades is. This was it; Mike was the person I needed to see. Mike was the specialist's specialist in his field. Mr. K would be delighted and I'd be allowed to keep running, and everyone would be happy.

I reached out to Mike, and to my amazement he was keen to meet me. I had no idea what to expect, except praying that he wouldn't say no to my running the impending London Marathon. At the time I was 46, a full-time working mum, with a pretty hectic lifestyle. Before TMRS my marathon training plan was haphazard, it consisted of running three times a week, and that was it. No strength sessions, no stretching or cool downs, or any other kind of cross training exercise. I developed an awful habit of my arms swinging across my body, whilst running, which was why my form was so terrible. I suffered with soreness in my lower back, and quite often pain in my calves shooting up to my knees. I had run a few half marathons before my first marathon in Brighton, the previous year. It wasn't the best experience, I finished in a very slow time around 5.30.

On first meeting Mike, I was fully committed and wanted to show him that I was fully prepared to work hard and do whatever it took. The alternative of not running, scared me senseless and just wasn't an option. I'd already discovered the benefits of the 'runners high' and just how important running was for my mental health and wellbeing. The first thing Mike did was film me 'running' on a treadmill from side and rear camera angles. This was fascinating, and equally mortifying now looking back. Then the real work began, initially Mike looked at my walking technique, which was dreadful. The first change was that I had to stop using a handbag for work, and use a rucksack instead, which would help my technique and improve my general posture. Relearning how to walk is trickier than it sounds, I should know, I've been there, and done that twice already as an adult. To go through the process again for a third time in seven years, was a defining moment. Obviously, this time I had Mike coaching me, which was a game changer. I soaked up every word and instruction and threw myself at the activation exercises and backwards walking, even though I didn't understand the methodology behind it back then. It was a revelation! Once you've got it, it quickly becomes second nature. Then we moved onto the business of sorting out my running technique. Learning how to run correctly, was surprisingly exhausting both physically and mentally, at first, I found it all consuming, but to be fair I was obsessed. I was so determined to change everything right there and then, all at once. I would quite often go to sleep at night, thinking about running routes, but now I was also dreaming about the movement of my arms. The first couple of times I practiced the technique outside of The Running School, I was to focus on my arms, and only think about the rhythm, and the angle. I was used to running long miles by this point but running just short distances properly was really hard work. Mike said, "Don't worry about your legs at the start, they will follow, just focus on your arms." I'm not exaggerating when I say I slept 'like a log' after those first few practice runs.

We didn't have much time before London, so Mike convinced me that run / walking was the best plan. I hadn't trained properly for long enough and physically I wouldn't be able to run it continuously, so I had to incorporate lots of walking too. I did lots of DMS, and strength and conditioning work. My time was slow, but that didn't matter, I'd done what I'd set out to do, and finished in one piece. In just a few weeks, under Mike and the team's watchful eye, I'd learned so much about my body and the way that it works, and it was incredibly empowering.

Before going to The Running School, I felt my body was against me, I'd been through so much physically and mentally because of cancer treatment. After the London Marathon, I knew I wanted to be a better runner, I wanted to try trail running in particular, and ultra-running would be the ultimate goal. Mike and I had a debrief, and discussed my game plan, admittedly I think I probably shut my eyes whilst telling him, squirming as I fessed up. He was amazing, he just nodded and smiled and said that he'd known all along, that this was the journey I'd take.

The great thing about training with Mike, is that there is nowhere to hide. He knows if I have done too much, worked too many hours, if I've got a niggle. He sees everything. He knows the sound of the way I walk and run. The first thing I noticed was that my upper body shape changed, quite quickly, my shoulders became defined, for the first time ever I had biceps. My performance and style transformed. I was running much faster and stronger, for longer periods of time, and crucially without any injuries. The achy back, and lower leg pains had long gone. Incredibly through running, my bone density results showed as though, I had never had treatment for cancer or been through the menopause. My fertility consultant at UCLH, was actively telling me to keep running and do whatever I was doing. The health benefits for me, were astounding and a 'no brainer'. I could not believe the progress I was making on Strava (I love reading my running stats). I even started running with a group of likeminded runners, that I met through Instagram, the majority were at least 10-20 years younger than me. With my newly found confidence and strength, I discovered that I was easily holding my own against them.

There's nothing I love more than training on one of Mike's plans. If I'm being brutally honest the races are almost secondary. I love the challenge of the steady progression, and the discipline. Since running at TRMS I've done lots of sub two-hour half marathons, and ran two marathons a month apart and achieved personal bests at both; 4:19 in London and 4.09 in Edinburgh. All of these achievements I'm immensely proud of, but it's a team effort. There is a genuine vested interest across the whole team at TRMS, they possess that incredible gift of making you feel like you are the only client on their books. For someone like me, especially because I'm so new to running in general, it's a wonderful inspiring space, in that it's not intimidating in the slightest. There is none of that machismo testosterone fuelled rubbish so often found in gyms, it's the complete antithesis of this.

I guess the most important part, is what I'm going to say next. Without question running has certainly defined me, but not cancer. The feeling of running in the cold, when my fingers are numb and I can't feel my face, the feeling of knowing that however hard I think it feels in that moment, it will never ever hurt as much, or be as hard as the pain during my recovery post-surgery. It's moments like these that make me feel most alive. Mike and I have discussed this many times, about the inner strength we can harness, through the power of movement. It's my way of keeping on and coping with whatever life throws at me. As much as I'd love to write solely about my running achievements. The main reason I came to Mike in the first place was to learn how to move properly. During the time I have been at TMRS, I've had to undergo a number of surgical procedures, all related to my ongoing treatment at UCLH, I also stupidly fractured the 5th metatarsal on my right foot in the summer of 2019. There is that old adage that there's nothing worse than an injured runner, in my case, times that by ten and you'll be somewhere near it. I am truly awful when I can't run, gnarly is a polite way of putting it. Each time Mike has coached me through rehabilitation and back to running fitness. If he tells me to rest, I do it. Coincidentally that's exactly what I'm doing now, currently six days post op from another procedure. This one has kicked me harder than usual, but the trust and belief I have in Mike and his team, know no bounds. Regarding the care and support, coaching and training, there is nowhere else I'd rather be.

I have absolute trust and faith, admittedly with teeth gritting patience, that Mike will get me back to where I need to be, at exactly the right time in my recovery. Put simply he is as important to me and my family as Mr. K is. I truly don't know where I'd be right now if I hadn't have met Mike when I did; probably with a litany of running injuries and ailments, and worse. Mike has opened the door and handed me the keys to a future I never dreamed existed, and for that I'm eternally grateful. Under his guidance, I fully intend to keep running as far into an indecent old age as I possibly can.

Mike: Judy is a cancer survivor. She first contacted us through social media and Nick said, "I think you are going to want to talk to this lady." The first time I met Jude it was like a whirlwind entered the centre.

"I had bone cancer; they used my fibulas from my legs to rebuild my jaw. I love running it helped me to survive, I want to run, I need to run, and I want to run London Marathon to give something back. I will do everything you tell me to do. Can you help me?"

I knew from the first five minutes of meeting her, that I couldn't stop her from running, even if she was in so much pain. I suspected that her consultants wanted her to see a running specialist, because they didn't want her to run and wanted someone else to tell her straight that she couldn't run!

I verified this was the case when I met Nicholas her consultant, a year later.

When I analysed Jude on that first session, she was in pain when running. She hit the ground very hard – a consequence of not being able to feel the ground during contact time – and she didn't use her arms much to propel herself forward, just to balance her side-to-side movements.

She had all the characteristics and compensations of someone who had been running with pain for a long time. She just wanted to move, irrespective of the pain shooting through her body. Like a lot of survivors from serious illness or injury and many elite athletes, she was mentally stronger than she was physically. Her philosophy was simple, "Put one foot in front of the other, keep going and don't give up until you absolutely have to."

We finished the biomechanical analysis and the movement analysis and when I explained what we needed to do get her moving efficiently, she said: "Great, will I be ready for the London Marathon in April?" The date was the 24th of February 2017, the London marathon was less than eight weeks away. I realised that Jude only heard what she wanted to hear.

So we started with walking re-education, as the compensations were similarly inefficient in her walking patterns and her running. But we focused on Jude's proprioceptive system using Dynamic Movement Skills, to reduce the force with which she hit the ground and try to get some feeling back in the lower part of the legs and the feet. Jude still does her DMS exercises daily.

I said that I would agree to her participating in the London Marathon if she interspersed walking with running because she would get injured, and it would take us much longer to fix the issues. Reluctantly after a few weeks of rehab and training she agreed.

When I get runners in, who feel sorry for themselves because they have had a minor injury and feel that it's the end of the world if they can't run, I introduce them to Judy! "John meet Judy Lewis, she is a runner too, but with a difference." They soon realise they do not have such a major injury after all.

Judy is an inspiration to us all and a non-stop motivating machine!

Everyone who meets her loves her enthusiasm and friendliness. After four years of working together, we still see her nearly every week. She was the instigator of the 'Ladies Only Running Evenings' and is currently training for her first ultra.

5

POOR MOVEMENT
PATTERNS & INJURIES

Over the last thirty years we have seen thousands of runners and although we are all wired differently and every runner is unique, we see similar running patterns which can be linked to inefficiency, pain, and repetitive injuries.

In the early days of The Running School, before the internet, analysis software, brilliant cameras, sensors, and Google, I used to categorise types of runners by the most common movement patterns that I analysed and we had cartoons drawn up to explain to people what they looked like. It wasn't the most scientific way of categorising runners (we will get to that part later in this chapter) but we found that most people could recognise their own running patterns using these cartoons. We had a lot of cheerful fun with runners explaining the details. But, reading this chapter, comes with a warning: You will never look at a runner in the same way again!

"The Shuffler"

"The Shuffler"

Shufflers look like they are running whilst trying to keep their slippers on. With very little knee lift and very low heel height, their running stride is inefficient and it's very difficult to pick up speed for several reasons.

1. Most of the work when running is done by the hip flexors and the quad muscles and not the power muscles (glutes and hamstrings) that drive a runner forward

2. Because there is little knee bend during the leg cycle, shufflers are always moving a long lever, which is slower to move than a short lever

3. Because they are running with a long lever, they often overstride, landing too far ahead of their centre of gravity and applying braking forces, which slows them down and increases their risk of injury

4. The arms have limited involvement in the running process and are stuck by the side of the body or perhaps they run with their arms in a long lever to compensate for what the legs are doing

"The Thumper"

"Thumper"

Normally, Thumpers are heel-toe (or heel strikers) runners who land very heavily on one or both feet while running. They land with the heel first and then the forefoot thumps on the ground hard in an uncontrolled manner. If they are running next to you in the gym on a treadmill you can hear the "thump-thump-thump" of their feet landing. It is so heavy that the treadmill vibrates. When running outside, the earth moves around them! This puts a lot of stress on the joints and can lead to shin and knee injuries.

"The Twister"

"The Twister"

The arms move across the centre line of the body rather than in a backwards – forwards movement and this leads to a twisting motion in the upper body.

The mid-section starts to rotate to compensate for what is happening with the arms, which in turn causes the legs to compensate and they begin to cross over the centre line of the body. If the runner has strong legs, then the rotation is mainly observed in the mid-section and the shoulders.

"The Weekend Warrior"

"Weekend Warrior"

These runners get the name from doing most of their training at weekends!

They are often involved in sport or have been involved in sport at some point in their life. We see it a lot with triathletes, footballers and rugby athletes, or men and women who go to the gym regularly but may not actually have a running background.

Weekend Warriors are generally strong and tend to adopt a fixed upper body position, tight shoulders, with the arms bent at the elbows but not involved in the running process, they are just held at the side. The rhythm comes from the shoulders rather than the arms.

Most of the running motion is carried out by the front of the thighs and is very quad dominant; the hamstrings and gluteal muscles are not involved as much as they should be and are not helping with the running biomechanics. They often overstride and frequently get injuries but just run through them.

"The Bouncer"

"The Bouncer"

The Bouncer has too much vertical displacement when running. They tend to have as much upwards and downwards movement as they have forward movement, which wastes a lot of energy and definitely doesn't help reduce running times. Often the higher they go, the more they collapse when they land, which is disastrous when it comes to injuries.

Very frequently, they are overstriding, meaning that they land ahead of their centre of gravity, which causes a braking action.

"The Octopus"

"The Octopus"

The Octopus runner seems to have little control of their limbs. When they run, it looks like each limb is working with its own independent motor control and moving in different directions. When the runner gets tired the arms and legs begin to flail just like an Octopus. The feet frequently point in different directions throughout the running cycle.

"The Slow Runner"

"Slow Runner"

The Slooowww Runner frequently has the characteristics of The Shuffler with a lot collapsing in their stride. The collapsing that occurs each time the single leg is on the ground puts a lot of stress on the knees, ankles and back. In most cases they would walk faster than they would run!

"KIDS"

"Kids"

Many young children, age 6-10 years, do not have full control of their body unless they have been involved with regular activity or sport from a young age.

Their running movements involve very short, choppy and fast steps, with a lot of noise when they are running because they are hitting the ground hard and with little upper body coordination.

When they try and run faster, they make one of two adjustments.

i) They may lengthen their stride as much as possible, which causes them to lean too far forward and sometimes lose their balance

ii) The majority, however, try and move their feet faster & faster with shorter steps. Because of the lack of coordination and because it's tiring, they cannot sustain this for long

Today the patterns are very much the same. But through experience and the help of technology we are able to analyse better and identify a specific issue that may be causing repetitive injuries or movement inefficiencies.

This list of movement patterns is by no means exhaustive. We would have to write a whole book on that alone. Instead, we will look at the most common and most impactful ones and explain the potential injuries they may cause.

The reasons why you are getting certain injuries shouldn't be a mystery and it isn't always just a case of "You need to stretch more." or "You need to do strength work." or "You need new shoes." Most of the time, there are clear reasons why you are getting injured – and that is because of the way you move and the amount of contact time you have with the ground when running.

One of the key reasons why we do a biomechanical analysis, and a functional movement examination is to identify inefficient movement patterns. The following examples are some of the most common, we hope you will be able to see for yourself why certain movement patterns cause pain and injury

Note: The following images are the movement patterns of actual runners who we have worked with – but their images have been traced to protect their individuality!

Excessive Overstride

What is It?

Overstride is probably the most common and most complex movement pattern in many runners. It is complex in the sense that it is linked to so many other movement patterns. However, it is also sometimes misunderstood.

When we talk about overstriding, we mean that you are landing <u>too far</u> ahead of your centre of gravity (C.O.G), in other words, you are landing <u>too far</u> ahead of your hips. We stress the words 'too far' because you should land just slightly ahead of your centre of gravity by about 3-4 inches,

C.O.G

but this depends on each person. You wouldn't want to land directly under your centre of gravity because by the time you load fully, your foot would be behind your centre of gravity, and this increases the contact time with the ground which causes different stress loads.

Overstride usually occurs when runners are running with an almost straight leg. They are using the anterior chain predominantly, that is the front muscles of the leg to propel the body forward. They are not bringing the heel up to utilise the power from their posterior chain muscles. The big power muscles, the glutes and the hamstrings.

It is important to note that an overstride can occur with a heel strike landing but also a forefoot landing, although the latter is more common with sprinters and with minimalist or 'barefoot' runners.

106

How can it affect you?

Impact forces:

When you land too far ahead of your centre of gravity it causes higher impact as you are loading the leg with more body weight, which can affect the ankle, shins, knee, hip and/or back.

Braking forces:

When you land too far ahead of your centre of gravity it causes braking forces, which slows you down. Think what happens when you are going downhill and trying to slow yourself down, you land with your feet ahead of your centre of gravity to slow yourself. The same effect will occur on flat ground.

Contact time on the ground & collapse:

Overstriding can cause you to spend more time on the ground since you touch the ground sooner in the leg cycle. Spending too much time on the ground will not only slow you down, but it will increase your risk of injury. This is largely because your body and joints have more time to collapse into poor alignments. For example, see sagittal collapse and knee valgus collapse sections.

Anterior dominant:

Runners who overstride, frequently land and run with a somewhat straight leg. When you land in front of your COG, you overuse your hip flexors when bringing your leg forward during swing phase. Driving forward with your hip flexors is not the best way to propel your body forward. In addition, you end up braking by using your quadriceps. To be efficient, you need to be using your power muscles, the glutes and hamstrings, to drive you forward.

Difficulty picking up speed:

When overstriding it is difficult to pick up speed. Runners who overstride are not using their power muscles in the posterior kinetic chain (glutes and hamstrings) and they are running with a long lever (straight leg). All these factors make it difficult to run fast, particularly up hill.

Poor Running Posture:

Often, runners who overstride, run leaning forward from the hips to compensate for the overstride or vice versa. As you lean forward, it becomes harder to activate the posterior chain muscle groups efficiently.

Common Myth

Many people believe that if you heel strike that you are automatically overstriding and that if you're landing forefoot, it stops you from overstriding. However, this is not the case. Runners can overstride irrespective of the foot strike they have. We see this regularly with runners who have decided to change their foot strike to forefoot. It is also possible to heel strike efficiently close to the centre of gravity.

Overstride and High Foot Inclination

Overstriding and landing with a high foot inclination could contribute to tibial stress (shin pain) due to the impact forces.   Landing with a high foot inclination, or high toe, means that the anterior tibialis (front shin muscle) overworks while trying to eccentrically control the forefoot from slamming down onto the ground. This sort of movement pattern will usually cause **muscular** shin pain at the front of the shin (anterior tibialis). In the left image, the anterior shin muscles need to work hard to control the foot from slapping down on the ground. In the right image, you will notice how the foot inclination is reduced once the runner improved his overstride.

Overstride and Forefoot landing (Plantarflexion)

C.O.G

Landing forefoot while over striding, puts extra stresses and forces through the calf and Achilles. In most cases, an overstride with a forefoot landing means the runner is landing with a high heel which increases the forces on the calf and Achilles while landing. Landing forefoot will not automatically stop you from over striding excessively. Many runners switch to forefoot and still land too far ahead of their centre of gravity resulting in calf, Achilles and hamstring pain.

The forces will predominantly go through the foot and the various muscles, bones and joints in the lower limb.

What Injuries is it linked to?

Knee pain:

It can cause knee pain because it increases the braking and impact forces. As mentioned in the previous chapter, these forces can range from three to five times our bodyweight. If you land too far ahead of your centre of gravity it causes higher impact through the landing leg when you strike the ground. This sends the landing shock up your leg and can have an impact on your knee among other parts of the body. Now imagine this happening every step for 10,000 steps when you go out for a 40 min run.

Shin splints:

It can contribute to tibial stress (shin pain) due to impact forces. But other factors linked with overstride, such as high foot inclination on landing can also contribute to shins splints. This sort of movement pattern will usually cause **muscular** shin pain at the front or the back of the shins and the calves.

Anterior hip pain/ groin pain:

Runners who overstride, can often be anterior dominant and/or run with a straight leg (long lever). This means that they are moving a long lever through the swing phase from the hip. Like a pendulum. If this is repeated thousands of times the repetitive nature will cause overloading and pain.

Back pain:

The impact forces can travel up the body and affect the back. Overstriding can cause back pain because it increases the braking and impact forces. The landing shock can travel upwards and can have an impact on several joints including the back.

Additionally, if someone has a forward lean to compensate for the overstride, this can cause stress to the back muscles (see picture)

C.O.G

111

Common Myth

You might have read or been coached to lean forward when you run because it will make you go faster. But the mistake that many people make after hearing this is that they lean forward from the hips (or bend from the hips). When this happens, the back muscles must support the torso in this position isometrically while also taking the loads of running.

Hamstring Pain:

Most people overstride by extending (straightening) the knee on landing, which puts the hamstring in a lengthened and vulnerable position when the leg gets loaded. Many runners complain that the hamstring pain gets worse after speed workouts. This is usually because the runner starts to lengthen their stride and go faster, meaning they overstride even more.

Low Heel Lift

What is it?

Low heel lift means that in mid swing phase, the heels are coming up to a point that is lower than the knee joint. In other words: less than a 90 degree bend at the knee joint. This generally indicates that the anterior muscles (the hip flexors, quads and TFL*) are the dominant muscles used to swing the leg forward. The leg swings forward as a long lever which usually leads to over striding in many cases. The quads then take over to both brake at contact with the ground and then carry and support the body through the stance phase This is why runners with low heel lift and an overstride generally feel their quads tiring before anything else in longer or faster runs.

A more efficient stride would have the heel coming above the knee level (a knee bend more than 90 degrees), then elastic reflex of the front muscles along with momentum to bring the leg/knee forward (rather than a driving through with the anterior chain).

* TFL or tensor fascia late

What injuries is it linked to?

Low heel lift is linked to anterior hip pain in that it usually means that the anterior muscles are over-working by repeatedly driving a long lever forward during the swing phase.

Sagittal Collapse

What is it?

During midstance, the body can sink too far down or collapse in the sagittal plane at certain joints (the ankle, knee, hip/trunk) and put extra stress on the joint and the tendons and muscles attached to it. This means that the runner is spending too long on the ground and the knee flexes (collapses) excessively and the ankle dorsiflexes at an excessive angle.

What Injuries is it linked to?

Achilles / calf pain:

Looking at the picture, we can see that the ankle is excessively dorsiflexed under the loads of the body. This position can overstretch the Achilles tendon, at the same time that your whole-body weight is being loaded on that one leg.

As you can see from the graphic above, the excessive angles can put pressure on the ankle, Achilles tendon or calf. (Note: Achilles tendonitis was the actual injury of the runner in the picture).

Knee pain:

While problems can occur if you run with too straight of a leg, if the knee bends too much or is positioned too far over the toe while bearing the full weight of the body it causes stress on the knee joint. Unfortunately, this is the exact position that some runners will collapse into while running. So, when the knee is flexed in this vulnerable position while the body is in full

114

weight bearing mode (midstance), it increases the stress on the knee joint. This can also lead to the knee collapsing into a valgus position.

Shin Pain:

When the knee bends too much in full weight bearing mode, the lower leg is in a vulnerable position. The lower leg was designed to support us under loads and stresses in a more upright position. When we load it at an excessive angle, it increases the stress and forces.

Back Pain:

When the trunk is in the position shown in the picture, the back extensor muscles will overwork under the loads of running.

Sagittal Collapse Improvement after Running Technique re-education

The below are snapshots of our runner both before and after changing running technique

Anterior Tilt

What is it?

The hip tilts forward and the spine arches to compensate for balance. This puts a mechanical strain on the spine, but also stresses the extensor muscles of the back. It can also put other joints out of alignment just as the SIJ, the knees, shins, and ankles. Anterior tilt can happen either in stance phase, in flight phase or both, but the risk of injury is really in the stance phase.

Anterior Pelvic tilt during mid stance: The glute max and med, play a major role in controlling the pelvis and stopping it from tilting forward when the foot is in contact with the ground. If the glute is not firing in time or there is a strength issue, then the runner can lose control of the pelvic alignment.

Anterior Pelvic tilt during flight phase: When in the flight phase of running, the core muscles are in control of the pelvis. If the pelvis is tilting forward excessively in flight-phase then it could indicate poor core muscle activation and/or tight hip flexors, which can pull the pelvis into this position.

What injuries is it linked to?

Back pain:

In most cases, when the pelvis is tilted, the body will compensate by arching the spine. Loading the body in this position can put a lot of mechanical strain on the back. This can also cause a compensatory bracing action in the mid and upper thoracic which can lead to stiffness.

Achilles pain:

Many people who have an anterior tilt also have a sagittal collapse. A runner with anterior tilt is usually anterior dominant and the firing sequence of the posterior chain is disrupted. Runners with anterior tilt who do not have much of a sagittal collapse may still be prone to Achilles injury due to the fact that they may actually be loading the body too far behind the centre of gravity, putting the ankle at an excessive dorsi-flexed angle.

SIJ / Hip Pain:

When in anterior tilt, the sacroiliac joint is more vulnerable to stress. So, loading the SIJ under the stresses of running in an anterior tilt can contribute to pain or injury.

Knee Pain:

Because an anterior tilt can be related to sagittal collapse and can interrupt the firing sequence of the glute and the hamstring, the knee can fall into a position of too much flexion or even a valgus collapse.

Contralateral Hip Drop

What is it?

This is where the hip muscles and glutes cannot control the pelvis and the non-weight
bearing hip side can drop (also, known as
Trendelenburg). This can put stress on the
lower back, the hips, IT band, knee, ankle and
feet as these joints are being over-loaded if they
are not in alignment. This drop can be due to
an activation issue or a strength issue or both.
There may be a delay in the glute and hamstring activation, or it could be due to a lack of
functional strength. It is also closely linked to
valgus collapse and will share many of the same
characteristics and problems.

What injuries is it linked to?

Knee Pain:

This inefficient alignment can put mechanical forces on the knee when loading. It can also put strain on the IT band. Since the IT band attaches at the
lateral side of the knee, the pain can be presented on the lateral side of the
knee.

ITB Pain:

This puts a strain on the IT band. Since the IT band, which is joined with
the TFL, attaches at the hip, pain from this can be presented on the hip,
down the side of the thigh or on the knee.

Ankle / Foot:

The ankle and foot will almost certainly need to compensate for the poor
alignment putting extra stress on the ankle/foot. Overpronation is the main
way the foot/ankle compensates for this poor hip alignment.

Achilles:

Because of the compensations of the foot and ankle (namely, overpronation) as mentioned above, the Achilles can often be loaded in a way that puts it under undue stress.

Back Pain:

When the non-weight bearing hip drops, the weight bearing side of the back gets compressed (A) and the side that drops (B) can get over worked trying to control the dropping pelvis (since the weight bearing glute is not doing its job). This can be due to either a delay in the glute activation or a weakness.

The body may compensate further up the kinetic chain and can also cause pain in the upper back/shoulders.

Valgus Collapse

What is it?

This is where the knee falls inwards towards the midline of the body. It puts a mechanical stress on the knee joint as it is being loaded under poor alignment. It often occurs with contralateral hip drop. Valgus collapse is a major contributor to over pronation. It is closely linked to both contralateral hip drop, crossing over and a lack of functional strength. This movement pattern will share many of the same characteristics and problems.

What Injuries is it linked to?

Knee Pain:

This poor alignment can put mechanical forces on the knee when loading. It can also put strain on the IT band. Since the IT band attaches at the lateral side of the knee, the pain can be presented on the lateral side of the knee.

ITB Pain:

This body alignment puts a strain on the IT band. Since the IT band, which is joined with the TFL, attaches at the hip, pain from this can be presented on the hip, down the side of the thigh or on the knee.

Shin Pain:

If the angle of the tibia is excessive, then this can put extra stresses on the tibia during loading.

Ankle / Foot:

The ankle and foot likely need to compensate for the poor alignment putting extra stress on the ankle/foot. Overpronation is the main way the foot/ankle compensates for this poor hip alignment.

Achilles:

Because of the compensations of the foot and ankle, the Achilles becomes loaded in a way that puts it under undue stress.

Cross-Over

What is it?

The foot crosses over the midline of the body during contact, which means that the full weight of the body is going through joints that are not in alignment, putting stress on the foot, ankle, knee, hip and back. This is also known as step width. It is closely linked to both valgus collapse and hip drop.

MIDLINE

What Injuries is it Linked to?

Knee Pain:

This poor alignment can put mechanical forces on the knee when loading. It can also put strain on the IT band. Since the IT band attaches at the lateral side of the knee, the pain can be presented on the lateral side of the knee.

ITB Pain:

As mentioned above, this poor body alignment puts a strain on the IT band. Since the IT band, which is joined with the TFL, attaches at the hip, pain from this can be presented on the hip, down the side of the thigh or on the knee.

Ankle / Foot:

The ankle and foot may need to compensate for the poor alignment putting extra stress on the ankle/foot. Overpronation is the main way the foot/ankle compensates for this poor hip alignment.

Achilles:

Because of the compensations of the foot and ankle as mentioned above, the Achilles can often be loaded in a way that puts it under undue stress.

Back:

If the biomechanics of the lower body change with step width, then it is likely that the biomechanics of the upper body will also change to compensate for poor alignment.

Over-Pronation

What is it?

Foot biomechanics are very complex, so we will not look at this from a podiatric point of view, but rather from a running and movement point of view. We focus on how general foot mechanics can be affected by the mechanics further up in the kinetic chain.

It is important first to highlight the difference between pronation and over-pronation. Runners often say that they had an analysis at a running store or a clinic and they were told that they pronate or supinate and they were recommended motion shoes or orthotics. Pronation is actually a very natural occurrence for all walkers and runners. Problems can arise when runners overpronate and there is pain!

When it comes to over pronation. There are a few important questions to ask: 'Is over pronation really the problem? Or does the problem come from further up the kinetic chain?' If the problem is actually coming from further up the kinetic chain, particularly from the arms crossing the midline or from the hips/knees, then would it not make sense to fix the issues at the arms hip or the knees rather than looking at shoe choice or orthotics first?

For example, in the graphic, our runner is overpronating and getting Achilles pain because of it. But you will also notice that our runner is also crossing the midline, which means that her ankle and foot will have to compensate. In this case, yes, the Achilles pain is caused by the overpronation, but the over pronation is actually caused by crossing the midline, which in turn is caused by poor hip mechanics. You will have already read how contralateral hip drop, valgus collapse and crossing over can contribute to overpronation. So, is overpronation really the cause?

Another question we need to ask is: Is there pain? Because how do you truly determine if someone is overpronating since all of us are built so differently. The easiest way to determine overpronation is if there is pain in the an-kle/foot/Achilles. If running re-education does not improve this, then the runner needs to be referred to a foot specialist. But in most cases, the pain caused by any overpronation goes away after the runner improves their tech-nique. Of the thousands of runners, we see every year, we only refer two or three to a foot specialist.

Some of the world's greatest distance runners have had excessive overpro-nation when landing, including Haile Gebrselassie.

What injuries is it linked to?

If there is overpronation, the areas that it will directly affect are the obvious areas: the foot, ankle and Achilles. The reasons for this are fairly obvious. The foot, ankle and Achilles go into poor alignment putting extra stresses on them while loading on one leg.

Excessive Plantar Flexion in Swing Phase

What is it?

During and after toe-off, the foot/ankle is excessively flexed or pointed.

Excessive plantar flexion at toe-off: It indicates that the calves might be over working to try and propel the body forward.

Excessive plantar flexion during swing phase: the foot stays in a pointed position through the whole swing phase then the calf is over working all the time.

What injuries is it linked to?

Calf pain:

When a runner toes-off excessively and keeps the ankle flexed it means that the calves get overworked and stressed.

Achilles pain:

The Achilles overworks on toe-off and in swing phase.

Hamstring pain:

This may seem like a strange result from pointing your toes, but Plantar flexion can decrease glute activation, so the hamstring can come under extra strain if the ankle is plantar flexed during hip extension/knee flexion in the swing phase.

Inefficient Arm Movement

Our arms play a major role in running bio-mechanics. Arm drive is extremely important for speed, balance and rhythm, and is very unique to every runner. The length of the pendulum of the upper body can affect the length of the lever on the lower body. Any asymmetrical movement of the arms can cause or be caused by an asymmetrical movement of the legs. Arm movement or lack of arm movement can also affect the posture of the mid-section.

Limited arm drive:

Deliberately limiting the use of the arms, costs more energy than it does to use the arms efficiently. Lack of arm drive causes other compensations such as twisting of the torso. In addition, it is the backward arm drive that propels the body forward, so it is a crucial part of efficient running.

Crossing over:

This can cause both compensations in the upper body i.e., torso rotation or compensations in the lower body i.e., crossing over or overstride on the contralateral leg.

Excessive movement at elbow angle:

The acute angle of the elbow should not fluctuate too much during the arm swing as this would be an inefficient movement. This is especially for distance running – elbow angle will fluctuate more in sprinting.

Long Lever:

A long lever is more inefficient to move when running. In addition, it often leads to a long lever with the legs, which is linked to the inefficiencies of overstride.

The acute angle of the elbow should be 45-60 degrees or less, especially for distance runners.

Head Posture

One thing we must not forget to mention is head posture. The whole body is involved in running – including our head.

Head position plays a major role in the posture of the rest of the body as well as the biomechanics. Poor head position can be a compensation from poor posture, or the head position is a compensation for what is happening further down the kinetic chain. For example, if someone is leaning forward from the hips, the neck, is in an extended position just to keep the head level.

Inefficient Motion

Now that we have seen snapshots of movement patterns that cause injury, we are going to look at examples of inefficient running motion. There is so much you can see by looking at overall running motion that you cannot see by slowing down and taking a snapshot. For instance, you can see if the running motion is fluid or if the person is limping or if the landing is louder on one side than the other. The best way to see this is to watch someone running live or by watching a video. In a book this is a little bit more difficult to do, so we will look at a series of photos and explanations. Let's look at the leg cycle and the arm drive.

LEG CYCLE

Inefficient Leg Cycle

Before looking at what an efficient leg cycle looks like in the next chapter, it is helpful to understand what an inefficient leg cycle looks like. In the following set of images, we will explain the sequence of the stride, starting with toe off of the left leg.

Look at the left leg from toe-off in the above image. As the foot leaves the ground, the foot stays low to the ground through the swing phase and then lands with a fairly straight leg in an overstride. This is inefficient for four reasons:

1. The runner is overstriding which adds braking forces to the running stride
2. The runner is spending too much time on the ground. There is barely any flight time
3. The runner is wielding a straight leg which is a long lever rather than a short one.
4. The runner is using the hip flexors and quads to drive the movement rather than the power muscles at the back – the glutes and hamstrings

RUTH'S STORY

Ruth Roberts
Recreational Runner

I run for the freedom. I run because when I feel physically strong, there is no glass ceiling in my mind. I run because it shakes the crumbs off the tablecloth of life. I am no Olympian – my running is anything from my commute to an excuse to eat cake – but when the trainers go on, a part of me believes I could be.

I ran my first marathon at twenty-six and roughly ten years, lots of adventures and 1000s of miles later, I might as well have been paying my physiotherapist's mortgage. It was like someone had poured superglue in my calves, especially the left one. Even the call to arms at a zebra-crossing could bring tears to the eyes if I crossed too enthusiastically. He kept needling and massaging the problem away until he bravely said, "*I can keep fixing you, but your issue is biomechanical, it's got to be technique. Go and see Mike who I've never met but I heard he's great.*"

Runners are stubborn by our very nature and I thought I knew plenty about running simply in the act of doing it. Surely you can either run, or you can't? Am I just handing over cash to be told what I know, or worse, that there is no hope for me? What if they think I'm a fake and just not fit enough? But I could barely walk and had just dropped out of the London marathon with only weeks to go – so anything was worth a try.

It took Mike approximately thirty seconds to find out what was wrong with me.

Overstriding, unstable hips, weak glutes, hamstrings not firing, bad posture. A few tiny adjustments in that moment on the treadmill and I already felt stronger. Knowing how normal I was, was the first big comfort. Knowing it was fixable if I put in the work, was the second. Knowing it was not only fixable but that I had untapped resource that will make my running easier, more efficient, and faster, was the third. Today I look at runners and the vast majority display some level of these issues.

In short, my calves were being massively overloaded. It all made sense. For years, I'd compensated by relying on my quads and hip flexors to swing my legs and they'd always scream the loudest at the end of a run. Eventually, the calves said, 'Too much!' Mike and the team's first goal was to fire up the glutes and the hamstrings. In that very first session, we did seemingly basic activation exercises and the results were rapid. Learning how to run from scratch was no doubt going to be exhausting but I could see and feel the results. My doubts were dispersed, I was all in and ready to heal.

I loved the lack of gadgets in the diagnosis. The running world is so full of tech and noise, but I've always been most attracted to the purity of it. Of course, The Running School has the cameras and state-of-the-art technology, but they are just a bonus. Mike's eyes and experience, and the way he trains his own team, are more valuable than any machine will ever be.

A year or so after my first round of sessions, the calf issue blew up again but this time on the other side. By the time I got back to The Running School, the scar tissue deep inside the right calf, close to the bone itself, was a significant problem. I could feel it from the moment I woke up, like a rock that wouldn't shift, and no massage was fixing it. It had become the most significant injury I've ever had, and it put me out of action for a total of about eighteen months. I pick up niggles from nowhere but, in my body, they last. An ache from out of the blue can persist for several weeks – or in this case, much longer. My lesson here was deal with it, don't live with it.

It was all originating from the back, manifesting itself in the lower legs. But through hard work, a lot of band work and strength work and Mike's constant efforts and enduring support, I'm now stronger than I've ever been.

Not only are we all a bit different, so too do our bodies change. Mike and his team know this better than anyone and they somehow make it feel like your superpower.

The Running School also understand me as a person. I like detail, to understand both the problem and the solution. I like to know what's important and what I can let go of. With every person who walks into the School, Mike is quietly weighing up their psychology as well as their biomechanics, working out how to get the very best from them without them even noticing.

When I was back up and running in short bursts when we were winning the 'Calf War' I was reluctant to run for longer distances. Mike encouraged me to enter the local 5k parkrun. He never forces me to do anything, he just cleverly suggests things, but this was the first time he was fairly blunt. I have always respected parkrun but didn't see the point for 'someone like me'. I can run 5k anywhere, anytime, after all. But as soon as I turned up and started running, I had to smile - Mike knew me better than I knew myself. In a big crowd like this, the competitive instinct kicked in. If I was running alone, I would have almost certainly stopped every five minutes, not wanting to push my calf to a fresh injury. Yet here I was, pain free, completing my first 5k in a year. With Mike's help, I'd broken through a huge mental barrier. We'd officially won the fight.

During the pandemic, the re-opening of the Running School became my sanctuary of normality and escape. I've never run better than I do now. I sometimes feel like I float across the ground – a feeling I know to mean I'm nailing it. I still want to get faster and beat what I call personal World Records, but I'll take running pain-free and care-free. In October 2020, I ran the Virtual London marathon on a last minute 'why not' whim, signing up just four weeks beforehand. I knew my mind was strong enough, but I'd not prepped my body well for such a distance in terms of practising hydration & fuelling. Mike didn't even blink when I told him what I was up to. My core strength, technique and confidence were unfaltering. Add in two great friends from The Running School and the spirit of Londoners cheering me on, it was the best day of the pandemic by far.

Today I get niggles in my hip – probably because my 'working at home' office chair is far from great. Back mobility and hip flexor stretches are my new best friends. My usually very-mobile-ankles have become quite stiff, probably because of the 2021 lockdown reducing my overall movement. They're all kinks that we recognise and iron out. I have some virtual races lined up, so I still have goals. I fully intend to be that 80-year old completing the London marathon in front of the cheering masses.

I can walk into the Running School and train next to an ultramarathoner or a stroke patient, a 10-year old or a professional rugby player, and of course someone just like me. The Running School doesn't care where you came from, it cares where you want to go. We all matter, and everyone gets treated in equal measure. To anyone who's ever said they can't run, that their knees are shot, that they're just not built for it, needs Mike in their life, because nothing could be further from the truth.

Mike: What you first notice when Ruth walks into the Speed & Rehab centre is the beaming smile that genuinely says, "I am pleased to see you and to be here." She is pleased to be there even when she knows the session will hurt and even if she can't run because she is injured. She will focus and give 100% to her rehabilitation, because that is what she does in her work and in her running. She is friendly and unpretentious striking up conversations with anyone who is training in the centre.

The smile was missing the first time we met for a biomechanical analysis. Five years ago, in 2016.

She had had some running injuries, but his one was particularly hard to shake off and her physiotherapist suggested she come and see us. Ruth understood straight away when I explained what I thought was the problem and how we would fix it. But she followed it with several questions: How long it would take? What would we be doing exactly? Would she have to stop running? How many times per week? Is there homework?

We managed to fix the first calve issue by changing the technique and focusing on activation of the correct muscle groups. Ruth had a busy schedule travelling with work and would pop in when she was in the UK and her work schedule allowed, or if she picked up a niggle.

She had an injury to the opposite calf a year later which proved to be a challenge and kept her off running for a long time.

Besides being deeply passionate about everything she does. Ruth puts her heart and soul into her work and her running and other past times. She is also multi-talented. She is an award-winning director and producer of documentaries, has won Emmy's and Baftas and has worked with and produced one the world's greatest story tellers David Attenborough. She is also a particularly good jazz singer and an all-round lovely person.

My role is to help her stay injury free, so she can achieve her running ambitions.

6

RUNNING RE-EDUCATION
THE RUNNING SCHOOL METHOD

I have been fascinated with running and speed since I started coaching forty years ago. Not just straight line running like track and cross country but also the differences between sports-specific running and speed development.

I was always intrigued when watching people run and I still am today. I began to notice the differences, when I started coaching young children from the age of six. I could see the movement patterns develop with the different age groups and how the movements changed again when they go through growth spurts and then through puberty and leading into adulthood.

They start off being fluid and elastic in their early years and then slow down by the time they have reached eleven or twelve. Some become uncoordinated and have limbs flying in different directions due to growth spurts and then subsequently lose their confidence. Puberty affects their biomechanics, making some of them clumsy and uncoordinated. Some are early developers and look like adults, while the late developers still look like children at sixteen. Some children run without effort while others run as if their life depend on it but seem to be going nowhere fast.

Some people seem to run without much effort at all and look so serene and smooth as if their feet do not touch the ground. You know the people I'm talking about. Everything they attempt from running to football, tennis, golf, even training for a marathon they seem to be good at without trying too much!

Coaching means teaching. When I have taught someone how to change or improve their movement to reduce pain or increase functionality, I get a sense of achievement. Anyone can train you and make you tired. A good coach should teach you **how** to move and run better.

We have taught thousands of people how to run.

Our array of athletes (we call everyone an athlete) range from people who have never run before in their life to individuals who are learning how to run again after injury or surgery. From elite runners and sprinters who have represented their country and won gold medals at the Olympics and World Championships, Ultra runners who regularly run 100 miles for fun, professional triathletes, professionals from football, rugby, handball, basketball and many other team sports. Then there are the thousands of recreational runners and children of varying abilities.

The process of changing movement patterns and improving the way we run is the same for recreational and elite runners! We change the movement patterns, by changing the biomechanics and stimulating the nervous system.

There are no bad runners; just runners who haven't been taught how to run! Or runners who don't practice enough.

I have many people come to see me who want to have the 'Perfect Running Technique' so they can run faster. They are surprised when I say it doesn't exist. What does exist is the perfect technique for you and your body and what you want to achieve.

Because we all have different movement maps and because the older we are, the more hard wired we are, it is impossible to impose one running technique on a person and say, "Do it this way or don't do it at all." For example, when it comes to foot strike, many people find it impossible to run on the balls of their feet, it causes them extreme pain in the calves and in the Achilles tendon, but it doesn't mean they can't run, it just means we have to adapt their running technique to suit them.

> For most of us, the technique is 70% generic, that is the technique drills and coaching ques apply. But about 30% of the change are very individual, because of our movement background and any injuries. So we have to make small refinements to achieve better efficiency.

Of course, there are a few key characteristics on how to move the legs and the arms correctly and in the right sequence, to achieve forward momentum.

But one thing is for sure, we all must practice and the more we practice the better we get.

What we are going to teach you here is how to change or improve your existing running technique, to one that will help you run better, run faster and more importantly, help you enjoy your running even more.

The simple fact is that most people have not been taught *how* to run. They may be taught how to *train* for running but have not been taught running technique. They assume it's something that comes naturally. But running *is* a skill! and just like any other skill it can be taught and it can be learnt.

4 Stages of Learning a new skill

When learning any skill whether job-related or sports-related, there are 4 stages to the learning process. We describe the stages below, but we will do so in terms of running technique:

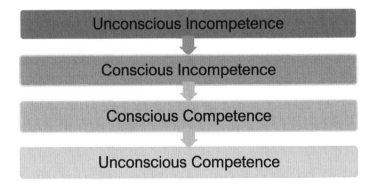

137

UNCONSCIOUS INCOMPETENCE

In this stage, a runner doesn't know why their running technique is not efficient or is unaware which elements of running technique are inefficient or causing injuries. This is because their movement maps have been developed over a long period time. They know something is not quite right but don't know what it is. Repeated habitual movements over the years change the movement maps in the motor cortex.

Most of our runners are surprised when they see on video how they run and say: "I didn't know I was doing that."

CONSCIOUS INCOMPETENCE

The runner is now aware that their running has inefficiencies and/or is contributing to injury and is aware of what movement patterns are causing this.

Now they can start making the necessary refinements and practice the skills to improve the technique. There is no doubt that this is the hardest stage in changing running technique as it takes concentration, practice, and the willingness to make the changes, and that comes before you start to feel the benefits. It is also more difficult for adults than it is for children because as adults we have been repeating the same patterns for years and we do not have to think of our movement. We are now taken outside our comfort zone. Change is only possible with concentrated practice and repeated effort.

CONSCIOUS COMPETENCE

The running technique has improved dramatically, and the runner now sees and experiences the benefits of the new technique. But it may be the case that the technique breaks down when the runner is tired or not consciously focusing on making the changes. The new movement patterns have not yet been wired into a new map. This stage improves with focus and practice until the new skills finally 'click' into place. Depending on the level of fitness it can take time to get to the next stage.

UNCONSCIOUS COMPETENCE

Through practice and repetition the new skill becomes 'unconscious' that is the brain passes it on to reflexive behaviour. The control of the movement becomes more automatic and can be performed without consciously focusing on the individual movement of the arms and the legs. Now the runner has created a permanent movement map of the new running technique.

If you would like to see many examples of runners changing their running technique, go to our Instagram page or our website:
www.instagram.com/therunningschool
www.runningschool.com

THE PROGRAMME

8 WEEKS TO BETTER RUNNING TECHNIQUE

How long does it take for me to change my technique? Is probably one the most frequently asked questions, from the time I set up the Movement & Running School. To make a new movement map 'unconscious'. We have found that the majority of runners can improve their technique in six to eight weeks. But... and there are a couple of buts!

The first 'but' is you must have a willingness to change your movement patterns and be prepared to put in the effort.

The second 'but' involves fitness levels. The fitter you are the easier it is to pick-up the technique and fine tune the changes. If your level of fitness is not sufficient or you have an injury, then the brain and the nervous system must work harder to cope with the cardiovascular development and it may take a few weeks longer. It doesn't mean you cannot start changing your technique until you are fully fit. In fact, you can use the running drills and short intervals to change your technique and improve your endurance.

Improving your technique requires practice. Like any new skill, it is important that the lessons and the homework sessions are completed weekly. Otherwise, too much time passes between sessions for any refinements to happen and for the movement to be learned by the nervous system and re-wire the movement map.

Whatever your level of running, you are likely to make some dramatic changes to your running technique in eight weeks – even to the point of unconscious competence. If you are an experienced runner and have had injuries in the past, you may be compensating unknowingly. The new technique will help refine your running movement and make it more efficient. You may just be making smaller changes in the beginning. But the knowledge you gain from these sessions will enable you to keep making improvements throughout the rest of your running career.

In this section, we will take you through how to use the arms, how to use the legs, how to land efficiently, but also how to tweak and refine your technique based on some common mistakes that runners make.

These changes will eventually help you run more efficiently and help you to avoid injuries through:

- Spending less time on the ground
- Having better body positioning
- Activating the right muscle groups
- Having better proprioception

BEFORE YOU BEGIN:

Before you begin this process, there are a few things you need to be aware of:

1. What to Expect

When we make running re-education changes after injury or for better running efficiency, we are changing the movement maps of the body and the brain. This means that we are making both physical and neural changes. Therefore, we do a lot of repetition during the practice drills… **Repetition is crucial!**

In the beginning - and depending on your level of fitness - it will be more tiring when you try the new running technique versus your 'current' running technique. The new technique will feel different at the beginning for the following reasons:

- The technique is a new movement map, so it requires concentrated practice initially
- The technique is being exaggerated in the earlier sessions as this will help you learn the movement better
- New muscle groups are working to propel the body forward (this is a good thing in the long run) the brain and nervous system are working to create new movement maps. This will make you faster because you will be spending less time on the ground. You will find that after the 4th or 5th week that your brain and body are adapting to the new technique

WHO TAUGHT YOU HOW TO RUN?

2. How to Practise

We recommend that you complete one running lesson per week and then complete the running homework for that week. The homework includes an additional two running technique sessions and incorporates mobility and strength exercises. The homework is described after every lesson.

Read Lesson 1 then practice the 'Technique Session' twice more during that week. Once you've done that you can move onto Lesson 2 followed by practice sessions 2-3 times during week. See week schedules.

If your level of fitness is not where you want it to be. You can use the 8-week program to both learn the new technique and get fit for running.

If you are injured and still in pain, then you need to wait until you can run pain free before starting.

It is human nature to want to try everything in one session! If you feel you are making progress more quickly, that's great, repeat the movements with a longer distance before you move onto the next lesson. On the other hand, if your fitness is not as good as you would like and you are making slower progress, then take your time and repeat any Lessons and Sessions that you feel necessary.

For Beginners:

We recommend that you follow the training program and go out and practice the technique sessions between two to three times per week. If you are used to going out a couple of times per week and just running, include the technique element in the first part of your run.

Don't try to implement your new technique during longer training runs at the beginning of the programme. Wait until week 4 or 5. Take your time. We all learn differently, so if it takes a couple of weeks more to pick up the technique or you need to practice more because your level of fitness is not where you want at the moment, that's okay. You are not under pressure to learn it within eight weeks.

For Advanced Runners:

Add these technique sessions into your training schedule in replacement of some of your training runs. Again, we recommend at least 2 to 3 technique sessions per week. If you are training for longer distances, you can always do the running technique sessions at the start of your longer run in the first 20-30 minutes.

Don't worry if you can't maintain the new technique in your longer run. Practice the session and the technique then revert to your 'current' technique so that you don't compensate and get tired. However, you may be surprised at how taxing these sessions are on your nervous system. Try a few practice sessions out to see how you feel the next day before adding to any of the sessions. You will find that after the 4th or 5th week you will be able to sustain the new technique over longer runs.

PLEASE REMEMBER THAT THIS IS A GUIDE AND YOU SHOULD TAKE INTO CONSIDERATION YOUR LEVEL OF FITNESS AND ANY INJURIES OR NIGGLES YOU MAY HAVE. DO NOT RUN IF YOU HAVE PAIN!

Also, please remember there is no one-size-fits all to this programme. If you feel you are benefitting from certain drills or exercises more than others, then adjust as necessary.

HOW TO USE THIS PROGRAMME

1. Read the rest of the Chapter on Running Re-Education, the cues and guidance
2. Plan where you are going to do your sessions
3. Re-read the technique guidelines
4. Warm-up
5. Follow the session plan for each week
6. Review
7. Do the weekly homework
8. Start a journal to write down how you feel before, during and after

Before you start, video yourself running. Get a friend to take a video of your current running technique. One from the side and one each from the back and front. You can use your smart phone or a camera for this. This will help you to see your progress after you have finished the full programme. Take the same videos again and compare your before and after's.

Technique Session Breakdown

Each technique practice session will consist of:

1. *Warm-up (10-15 minutes, 20 minutes if it is cold)*

- Warming up is especially important when doing technique drills since you will be practicing new movements and using new muscles. Follow the drills in the warm-up section of the Exercise Library. Our warm-up is designed to prepare your cardiovascular system as well as your proprioceptive system. You can do your own warm-up if you prefer. Just make sure of one thing... that you do warm up.

2. *Pre-Session Activation Exercises*

- These are designed to get the right muscles activated. This will help reduce injury due to compensation, but also fire the muscles in the right sequence. The proprioceptive exercises train your body to react with the ground more quickly.

3. *Running drills (45 to 60 minutes)*

- The time you can spend practicing the running drills will depend on your level of fitness. So, use your judgement and adapt, as necessary.
- Recovery - depending on your level of fitness you can use a walk back recovery or jog back recovery if appropriate for your setting/location. After the first 10 runs aim to have at least 60-90 seconds recovery before each run.

4. *Post-Session Activation Exercises*

- These are optional. If you have the time and you are not feeling too fatigued, then try to include these in your session.

5. *Cool-down & Mobility (10-15 minutes)*

- Now that your body is warm, it is an optimal time to work on your mobility – especially in problem areas such as the hip flexors. Cooling down will help reduce any muscle soreness after you do the drills.

6. Strength Session

- We have included some key strength sessions for you to try on the days you are not running. Make sure you do the warm-up before you try these exercises.

PLANNING A SESSION

Where to hold your sessions:

These sessions can be carried out at a track, in a park or just a long stretch of grass. We recommend that you practice outside.

Park, field or green area

Mark out a 50m and 100m stretch. For some of the longer runs, you will need to mark out up to 400m. The measurements do not need to be exact – just approximate, you can pace it while warming up. Bear in mind that if you feel you need to run more than 50m to get the rhythm of the new technique then do so.

Track

Everything is measured out for you.

VERBAL COACHING CUES

As discussed in the movement section, we take in information visually, kinesthetically and auditorily. When we coach runners in our centers, we use all these methods to help with the learning process of improving their movement patterns.

Visually, they get feedback using mirrors or videos.

Kinesthetically, they get feedback from their own proprioceptive system i.e., body awareness.

Auditorily, they get verbal feedback from a coach through coaching instructions and cues.

Since we are unable to give you those in real time, we have included some of them into your lessons so we will explain these to you. These verbal coaching cues will help you to remember what to do during your practice runs. Not all the cues may make sense to you as you read the list below, but you can refer to them as you are going through your lessons.

Verbal Coaching Cues

Lower Body

'Cycle Up' – this cue will help you to remember to keep the heels coming up past the height of the back of your knee and help you spend less time on the ground. Remember, it doesn't mean flick your heels up. There should be a cycling motion as per the instructions in Lesson 1.

'Lead with the heel' – a reminder not to plantar flex (point your toes) after toe-off. Imagine your heel leading the leg cycle motion. This will take the pressure off your calf/Achilles and help you to activate your glutes. (See Lesson 3)

'Soft knee' – a reminder not to extend/straighten the knee just before landing. This will reduce your overstride if the 'cycle up' verbal cues doesn't reduce an overstride.

'Aim for Midfoot' – if the 'cycle up' cue hasn't reduced the angle of your forefoot or your heel strike, then you can use this verbal cue to help you. It still may mean that you land forefoot or heel to toe, but that's okay, we're aiming for a modest angle.

'Stay light' - Feet should land lightly and the forces should feel equal on each foot. Listen to the sound to see if one foot is landing heavier than the other.

Verbal Coaching Cues

Trunk

'Body upright' - a reminder not to lean forward. If you are using your arms correctly you will not have to think of this

Upper Body & Arms

'Hip to chin' – a reminder to bring the hand back towards your hip with a bent elbow then back up to chin or shoulder level (see Lesson 1)

'Elbows bent' – a reminder to keep your elbows bent to an angle equal to or less than 60-90 degrees

'Drive elbows back' – a reminder to focus on the backwards motion rather than the forward motion. It also helps to keep the elbows bent.

'Relax shoulders' – a reminder not to brace or compensate by tensing the shoulders or the upper thoracic (upper back)

Head

'Head neutral' – a reminder not to compensate with the head, by either looking up, down or tilting to one side. This ensures that no compensations occur further down the body. It also plays a major role in the activation of the core.

Verbal Coaching Cues

General

'Find your rhythm' – once you are past making refinements, this is a reminder to just relax and find a rhythm that suits you. This will also help you feel what cadence works for you.

'Increase arm speed' – if you think your speed is too slow, just try moving your arms quicker (See Lesson 4)

WEEK 1

TECHNIQUE LESSON 1:
The Basic Changes - Leg Cycle & Arm Drive

When we begin the running re-education process, we start from the ground and move upwards – we start with the legs. The first thing we teach our athletes is how to 'cycle up'. This term best describes efficient motion of the leg, and we will explain further how to do this in this section.

We cycle up for several reasons. It causes us to land just a few inches ahead of our centre of gravity (hips) – so it stops us from over striding too much. Over striding is majorly inefficient and it contributes to many injuries.

It helps to prevent us from spending too much time on the ground. It makes the leg a short lever rather than a long lever (A long lever makes it difficult to pick up speed). To stop overstriding doesn't just mean changing our foot strike i.e., heel strike or forefoot. We want to change the way the whole leg moves.

The following explains the theoretical part of changing your technique. Read it over before going out and trying Session 1.

Leg Cycle

Efficient Leg Cycle

In the last chapter, we looked at what an inefficient leg cycle might look like. Now let's look at an efficient leg cycle. If you look at elite athletes, you will almost always see a similar leg cycle to the following.

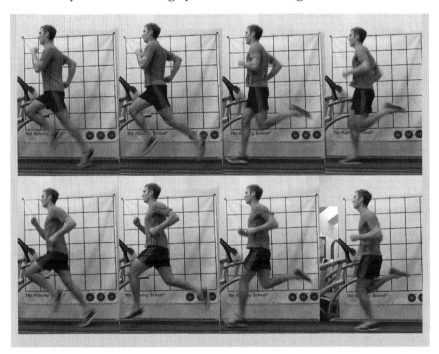

As the foot toes off, the hip extends, then the knee bends so that the heel comes up nice and high towards the buttocks. Then the leg comes through the swing phase as a short lever and lands just ahead of the athlete's centre of gravity (hips).

This is *efficient* for the following reasons:

1) The runner is not overstriding which means fewer braking forces to the running stride
2) The runner is not spending as much time on the ground since they are landing and toeing off closer to the centre of gravity. There is now more flight time
3) The runner is wielding a short (bent) lever rather than a long one
4) The runner is using the power muscles (glutes and hamstrings) to drive the movement forward

Leg Cycle Instructions

Verbal coaching cue: CYCLE UP

Now let's put this cycle pattern into practice. Practice this while standing to get a sense of what you will do while running:

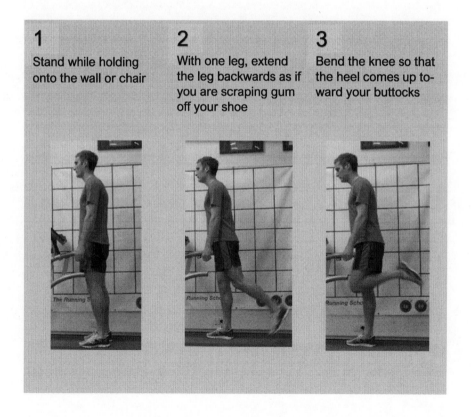

1 Stand while holding onto the wall or chair

2 With one leg, extend the leg backwards as if you are scraping gum off your shoe

3 Bend the knee so that the heel comes up toward your buttocks

4

Allow the knee to come forward in front of your body

5

Drop the foot down just ahead of your centre of gravity

The posterior chain power muscles (glutes and hamstrings) should be the dominant muscles in propelling the body forward. Extending your stride length the correct way is crucial. You need to use your glutes and hamstrings to create that propulsion.

ARM DRIVE

Efficient Arm Drive

The arms are especially important to the running movement. They give us balance, rhythm, speed, and they help to activate the core. The rhythm from the arm drive also helps to coordinate the leg cycle. Although the arm movement will vary slightly due to your own body shape, your mobility and your running speed, the general movement should follow these basics:

1

The **elbows** should be bent, loosely at the elbow 90 degrees or less for distance runners

We start the training lessons with arms bent at the elbow at 90 degrees, but on the runs, you will adjust your arm angle to where you are comfortable at 60 or 45 degrees.

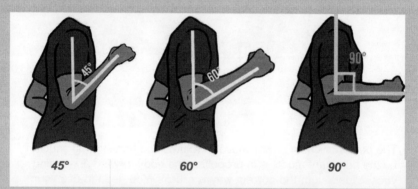

45°   60°   90°

2

The **hand** should be in a light fist as if holding a butterfly. The thumb should be over the forefinger.

3

The **wrists** should not be facing down, but they should be facing your body. This helps to keep the arm motion to go forwards and backwards and reduces the amount of twisting and helps promote good shoulder posture.

4

The elbow should **drive backwards** to the point where the hand meets the **top of the hip.** The backwards drive is especially important since that's the part of the arm motion that propels the body forward.

5

It should then **come forwards** so that your fist meets **just below the chin or shoulder** level. Note that the level that it comes up to can depend on your speed but for learning the new movement we will aim for chin level. This arm should come forwards more naturally than the backwards motion. If you focus on the forward drive of the arms, it will actually drive your body upwards. So, focus on the backwards motion.

6

The arms should **not cross the midline** of the body as this can cause twisting of the upper body and can cause compensations to happen on the lower body.

So now it's your turn to try it. Like with the legs, first try it standing before you try it running. It's helpful to try it in from of the mirror. Once you feel comfortable with it you can go out and try it with the running.

Now that you have tried the leg and arm motion while standing, its time you tried to put it in motion. **Start Week 1.**

WEEK 1 SCHEDULE

DAY	SESSION DESCRIPTION	DURATION
1	Running Technique Session 1	60 min
2	Walk or Rest + Activation/Mobility (Set 1)	45 min
3	Repeat Running Technique Session 1	60 min
4	Walk or Rest	30 min
5	Walk + Activation/Mobility (Set 1)	30 min
6	Repeat Running Technique Session 1	60 min
7	Walk or Rest + Activation/Mobility (Set 1)	30 min

*Note: For Warm-Up, Activation, Mobility, Strength & DMS/Proprioception exercises, refer to the Exercise Library

*Note 2: If you are an advanced runner then you can replace your walk/rest days with your usual run or strength days.

Technique Session 1

Basic Technique Changes

Warm-Up: 10-15 Minutes

See Warm-Up Section OR Use your own Warm-Up

SESSION: 45 to 60 Minutes

Use walk or jog recovery in between the technique runs

Speed	Sets	Distance	Recovery Time	Focus
Medium Pace	5	50m	Jog back	Focus on your current running style. Do a few runs and pay attention to how you run without applying any of the new coaching tips
Medium Pace	6	100m	Jog/walk back	Cycle legs up
Medium Pace	5	50m	Jog back	Arm drive: chin to hip relaxed
Medium Pace	5	100m	Jog/walk back	Leg Cycle + arm drive
Medium Pace	5	100m	Jog/walk back	Leg Cycle + arm drive
Fast Pace	5	50m	Jog/walk back	Leg Cycle + arm drive

Exercises & Cool-Down: 10-15 Minutes

Activation/Mobility Set 1 + walk or jog

WEEK 2

TECHNIQUE LESSON 2:
Feedback from Session 1, Foot Strike & the Importance of Arms

---

Now that you've done a few practice runs, you've probably noticed a few things. In session 2, we are going to address some of those questions:

- Does it feel different?
- Does it feel like a lot of effort?
- Did your foot strike change?
- Did you automatically switch to forefoot landing?
- Did your posture improve?
- Did you feel lighter on your feet?
- Did you run lighter and faster?

COMMON FEEDBACK AFTER SESSION 1

It feels different

This is normal at the beginning. It feels strange for several reasons. It's a completely new movement to your brain and nervous system. You have been working on your own technique for years! Right now, it is difficult to get the neuromuscular coordination between the arms and the legs and you consciously need to think about getting the movement right. Be patient and persistent with this – it *will* come with practice.

It feels like a lot of effort

This is normal at the beginning. You are now using more muscle groups to drive you forward. In the long run, this will be more efficient. Keep in mind that you will also be exaggerating the technique in the beginning for your body to learn the new movements. You will adapt a personalised movement as the sessions go on. So again, be patient with this.

I am now landing forefoot

You may have noticed that you've gone from landing heel-toe to landing forefoot. The new leg cycle movement is more efficient so it can often automatically change your landing position to forefoot since you are now landing closer to your centre of gravity. However, landing forefoot is not for everyone and it may not be best for you in the long term. So, it may be more appropriate to land heel first or midfoot, especially if you are a distance runner.

Some of the reasons for this are

i) If you've run heel toe your whole life, it may take a very long time to switch to forefoot

ii) Switching to forefoot might not be ideal for your body type

iii) Switching to forefoot may not be ideal for your distance, pace or fitness level. As we mentioned previously, many elite marathon runners run heel-toe though they still land efficiently in terms of their speed overstride and centre of gravity. Elite runners on the track, will run forefoot. But bear in mind that they are running over 20 km/h in a 10000m race. Importantly, they are also running in spikes which usually force you to land forefoot

The key is this... everyone is different.

In your next practice session, notice how you are landing. While maintaining the leg cycle try switching from forefoot to heel strike and see what is more comfortable for you.

I feel more upright

A lot of runners find that the arms change their posture. If you start using the arms the way they should be used, it helps activate the core muscles and makes you more upright. It also stops your shoulders from rolling forwards which in turn improves your posture.

I feel lighter and faster

There are several reasons for this. You have stopped overstriding - landing ahead of your centre of gravity which causes a braking motion. The foot is now spending less time on the ground and you spend more time moving across the ground in flight phase. The leg cycle also focuses on the backward motion of the leg, which drives you forward. The backward motion of the elbow drives you forward. The coordination of the leg cycle and the arm drive work together beautifully to make you lighter and faster.

Coaching Points for Foot strike and Arm Drive

Foot strike:

Adjust back to heel strike or mid foot landing if that feels more comfortable for you. But you still need to ensure that you are landing close to your centre of gravity.

Arm Drive:

Do some runs to experiment with the arms to see how it affects both your biomechanics and your speed. For instance, try running with the new arms for 10 seconds then drop the arms completely for another 10 seconds. Take note of what happens to your technique. Does your torso start to twist? Do you lose your balance? Does your speed decrease? Or try running 10 seconds with the new arms then speed up the movement of the arms. What happens? Does your cadence increase? (See Lesson 2)

Arm Angles:

Experiment with different arm angles, which one feels better for you 90°? 60°? 45°?

WEEK 2 SCHEDULE

DAY	SESSION DESCRIPTION	DURATION
1	Running Technique Session 2	60 min
2	Walk or Rest + Activation/Mobility (Set 2)	45 min
3	Repeat Running Technique Session 2	60 min
4	Walk or Rest	30 min
5	Walk + Activation/Mobility (Set 2)	30 min
6	Repeat Running Technique Session 2	60 min
7	Walk or Rest + Activation/Mobility (Set 2)	30 min

*Note: For Warm-Up, Activation, Mobility, Strength & DMS/Proprioception exercises, refer to the Exercise Library

*Note 2: If you are an advanced runner then you can replace your walk/rest days with your usual run or strength days.

Technique Session 2

Foot strike & Importance of Arms

Warm-Up: 10-15 Minutes

See Warm-Up Section OR Use your own Warm-Up

SESSION: 45 to 60 Minutes

Speed	Sets	Distance	Recovery Time	Focus
Medium Pace	5	50m	Jog back	Pay attention to how your foot lands. Forefoot? Heel strike? If you've switched to forefoot since trying the new technique, try going back to heel strike to see if it feels more comfortable
Medium Pace	5	100m	Jog/walk back	Leg Cycle + arm drive + foot strike
Medium Pace	2	100m	Jog/walk back	Run 50m with arm drive then drop the arms and run 50m with no arm drive. Pay attention to what happens
Fast Pace	5	100m	Jog/walk back	Run 25m with arm drive then start driving the arms more quickly for the next 75m. Pay attention to what happens
Medium Pace	10	100m	Jog/walk back	Leg Cycle + arm drive
Fast	5	50m	Jog/walk back	Leg Cycle + arm drive
Own pace	4	Run 1 Min Walk 1 Min		Find your rhythm

Exercises & Cool-Down: 10-15 Minutes

Activation/Mobility Set 2 + walk or jog

WEEK 3

TECHNIQUE LESSON 3:
Common Mistakes & Making Refinements

Sometimes when we try a new movement that is not natural to us, we can start to compensate to try to achieve the movement.

Some of us start to do some pretty unusual and wonderful compensations with the legs and the arms. So, we will take you through the most common of these and explain how to correct them.

We will explain it and give you the coaching cues so that you can make the corrections yourself if you feel you are doing that compensation.

ERROR 1: Leg Flicking vs Leg Cycling

Some of us, in an effort to get the heel up, will just flick up using the hamstring – as if you were doing bum kicks on the spot. This does not propel you forwards and can put undue pressure on the hamstrings. You need the hip extension part of the leg cycle before you bring the heel up. This will create a cycle motion rather than a flick.

✅ How to Correct it

Cycle up: Imagine the heel/foot is drawing a circle in the air – not an arc – as you complete a full leg cycle.

Extend the hip: Think about extending the hip momentarily before cycling up.

ERROR 2: Plantar Flexing on Toe-Off

As we toe off, some of us may tend to point the toe. This can put extra stresses on the calf as you toe-off, but often runners will hold this position throughout the swing phase and keep the calf contracted the whole time – putting even more stresses on the calf. It also contributes to a late toe-off and can decrease glute activation.

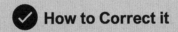 **How to Correct it**

Lead with the heel: As you toe off, imagine that your heel is leading the movement and cutting the air through the cycle.

ERROR 3: Over-exaggerated Arms

Sometimes when runners try the new arm movement, they exaggerate the arm movement too much. The motion may be too big, and they may bring the hands up past chin level. This can adversely affect your biomechanics in several ways.

1. Emphasising the upward motion of the arm drive, can drive you upwards rather than forwards and interrupts your rhythm
2. The large range of motion of the arms could slow down the cadence
3. It can change the way the leg cycles i.e., it would emphasise knee drive rather than the backward leg cycle that drives you forward

✅ How to Correct it

Drive the elbow back: Focus on the backward part of the arm drive. This will propel you forward.

Chin level or shoulder level: if you are having trouble aiming for the chin level, aim for the shoulder level.

ERROR 4: Arms opening and closing

As the arm comes forward there is a nice angle of less than 60-90 degrees. But as the arm comes back, you may open the elbow angle which turns the arm into a long lever. A long lever is more difficult to move around. But this can also affect the lower body biomechanics; a long lever up top can lead to a long lever below and cause the legs to overstride.

✅ How to Correct it

There are a couple of ways to correct this. The simplest way is to get in front of the mirror and practice. Shorten the angle. If it is 90 degrees, then go to 60 or 45 degrees.

ERROR 5: Poor pelvic Posture / Anterior Tilt

If you have tight hip flexors from doing a lot of sitting in your day-to-day life or even a lot of cycling, you may have an anterior tilt, meaning, your pelvis is tilted forwards.

This can cause a few injuries as detailed in the movement patterns section, but from an efficiency perspective, this position can deactivate our power muscles - the glutes.

This is not an easy thing to correct while running. First, you would really need to work on the mobility of your hip flexors and the activation of your glutes through activation and mobility exercises. Otherwise, you may find it to be counterintuitive to try and 'cycle up' with the heel while keeping a neutral pelvis (this is because of tight hip flexors). It is one of the most difficult changes to make if you do not work on your hip mobility first. However, there are some things you can try while running.

 How to Correct it

Increase Hip Mobility: It is important that your hip joint is mobile, this will assist with the running. Follow the hip mobility exercises regularly (See Exercise Library).

Use the Arms: Using the arms properly can help to activate the core muscles to improve your posture.

Keep a neutral pelvis: Again, this is very difficult to do whilst running, but you can try this: Imagine that your pelvic girdle is holding water. If you have an anterior tilt, water will be spilling out the front. But if you try to use your core muscles to tilt the pelvis back to a neutral position, the water should not spill out. This will come from a subtle adjustment using the lower abdominal muscles. You should not brace the core so hard that it wastes energy or makes breathing difficult.

ERROR 6: Continued overstride

In most cases, teaching a runner to cycle up will stop the excessive overstride from happening. But occasionally, some our habits die hard. A runner might cycle up, but they also might continue to extend/straighten the knee just before landing so it makes them land ahead of their centre of gravity. Don't be overly worried by this if you don't manage to correct it in the first few weeks. It may take you a little longer.

Below, our runner is cycling up nice and high, but when the knee comes through in swing phase, our runner straightens her knee and extends her foot out in front of her – causing her to overstride. She should have dropped the foot to the ground after then knee came through.

Below, our runner is doing the same thing - cycling up nice and high, but when the knee comes through in swing phase, our runner straightens her knee and extends her foot out in front of her — causing her to overstride even though she is about to land forefoot. She should have dropped the foot to the ground after then knee came through.

✓ How to Correct it

Once the knee comes forward in the swing phase, focus on dropping the foot lightly underneath the knee so that the shin is perpendicular to the ground as opposed to extending the knee to the point where it is almost straight. Think about landing on a 'soft knee' (slightly bent) rather than a straight knee.

WEEK 3 SCHEDULE

DAY	SESSION DESCRIPTION	DURATION
1	Running Technique Session 3	60 min
2	DMS (Set 1) + Activation/Mobility (Set 3)	40 min
3	Repeat Running Technique Session 3	60 min
4	Walk or Rest	30 min
5	DMS (Set 1) + Activation/Mobility (Set 3)	40 min
6	Repeat Running Technique Session 3	60 min
7	Walk or Rest + Activation/Mobility (Set 3)	30 min

*Note: For Warm-Up, Activation, Mobility, Strength & DMS/Proprioception exercises, refer to the Exercise Library

*Note 2: If you are an advanced runner then you can replace your walk/rest days with your usual run or strength days.

Technique Session 3

Technique Refinements

Warm-Up: 10-15 Minutes

See Warm-Up Section OR Use your own Warm-Up + Activation/Mobility Set 3

SESSION: 45 to 60 Minutes

Speed	Sets	Distance	Recovery Time	Focus
Medium Pace	5	50m	Jog back	Lead with the heel. Don't point the toes
Medium Pace	5	50m	Jog back	Arm drive: Focus on a short lever (keeping the elbow bent the whole time), driving the elbows back, and the chin to pocket movement
Medium Pace	5	50m	Jog/walk back	Leg cycle: make sure that you are not simply flicking the heels up toward your butt. Focus on cycling the heel in a circular motion
Medium Pace	5	50m	Jog/walk back	Leg cycle: make sure that as your knee comes forward you don't extend (straighten) your knee before landing. Instead, drop/place the foot underneath your centre of gravity
Medium Pace	5	50m	Jog back	Pelvis: If your pelvis is tilting forward and your back is arching, focus on adjusting the pelvis so that it is in a more neutral position. Don't brace with your core muscle to make the adjustment – it will inhibit your breathing
Medium Pace	5	100m	Jog/walk back	Focus on any of the above refinements that you need to work on
Own pace	5	Run 1 Min	Walk 1 Min	Focus on any of the above refinements that you need to work on

Exercises & Cool-Down: 10-15 Minutes

Activation/Mobility Set 3 + walk or jog

172

WEEKS 4 & 5

TECHNIQUE LESSONS 4 & 5:
Scaling Down and Cadence

So up until now, we have still been exaggerating the movement. We have been driving the arms from chin to hip. Cycling the legs so that the heels come up nice and high. As mentioned, this helps accelerate the learning process so that the brain and neuromuscular system learns it faster. However, that level of movement may not be appropriate or sustainable for your speed or distance.

Let's look at what may be happening:

Exaggerated movement & too slow cadence

Your movement is too big, and your speed is too slow. If you are running at a slower speed but trying to do a big range of motion with the arms and legs, you will actually end up spending too much time on the ground. In addition, the large movement is unnecessary and inefficient.

How to correct it

This one is easy, all you have to do is reduce the range of the arm motion but increase slightly the speed of the arms (and the legs). In other words, make the arm drive smaller and quicker. This should have an automatic effect on the leg cycle, making the leg cycle smaller, quicker and tidier as well. You will notice that it will be increasing your cadence. Now, you will be spending less time on the ground while also using an efficient leg cycle. Even though the cycle may be smaller at slower speeds than it is at faster speeds, we still need to make sure that the heel cycles up past knee level to promote activation of the power muscles.

Now it is your turn to go out and practice the different range of motion of the arms and legs as well as changes to your cadence and find the one that feels best for you and your speed.

WEEK 4 SCHEDULE

DAY	SESSION DESCRIPTION	DURATION
1	Running Technique Session 4	60 min
2	Walk or Rest + Activation/Mobility (Set 4)	45 min
3	DMS (Set 2) + Strength (Set 1)	45 min
4	Repeat Running Technique Session 4	60 min
5	Walk + Activation/Mobility (Set 4)	30 min
6	DMS (Set 2) + Strength (Set 2)	45 min
7	Repeat Running Technique Session 4	60 min

*Note: For Warm-Up, Activation, Mobility, Strength & DMS/Proprioception exercises, refer to the Exercise Library

*Note 2: If you are an advanced runner then you can replace your walk/rest days with your usual run or strength days.

Technique Session 4

Scaling Down

Warm-Up: 10-15 Minutes

See Warm-Up Section OR Use your own Warm-Up + Activation/Mobility Set 4

SESSION: 45 to 60 Minutes

Speed	Sets	Distance	Recovery Time	Focus
Medium Pace	5	50m	Jog back	Leg cycle + arm drive: Continue exaggerating the technique movement for a few runs so that you can compare the changes
Slow Pace	5	100m	Jog/walk back	Scale down the technique to match your slower pace. The movement should be smaller and the cadence might need to increase. Focus on being light and quick off the ground. Heels should still come just above 90 degrees (the back of the knee)
Medium Pace	5	100m	Jog back	Increase the pace to medium and adjust the technique to match it
Fast Pace	5	100m	Jog/walk back	Increase the pace to a fast pace and adjust the technique to match it
Own pace	4	3 minutes continuous	Walk recovery1 min	Find your rhythm and adjust your technique and cadence to match your speed

Exercises & Cool-Down: 10-15 Minutes

Activation/Mobility Set 4 + walk or jog

175

WEEK 5 SCHEDULE

DAY	SESSION DESCRIPTION	DURATION
1	Running Technique Session 5	60 min
2	Walk or Rest + Activation/Mobility (Set 5)	45 min
3	DMS (Set 2) + Strength (Set 1)	45 min
4	Repeat Running Technique Session 5	60 min
5	DMS (Set 1) + Activation/Mobility (Set 2)	45 min
6	Strength (Set 2)	45 min
7	Repeat Running Technique Session 5	60 min

*Note: For Warm-Up, Activation, Mobility, Strength & DMS/Proprioception exercises, refer to the Exercise Library

*Note 2: If you are an advanced runner then you can replace your walk/rest days with your usual run or strength days.

Technique Session 5

Scaling Down

Warm-Up: 10-15 Minutes

See Warm-Up Section OR Use your own Warm-Up + Activation/Mobility Set 5

SESSION: 45 to 60 Minutes

Speed	Sets	Distance	Recovery Time	Focus
Medium Pace	5	50m	Jog back	Leg cycle + arm drive: Continue exaggerating the technique movement for a few runs so that you can compare the changes
Slow Pace	5	100m	Jog/walk back	Scale down the technique to match your slower pace. The movement should be smaller and the cadence might need to increase. Focus on being light and quick off the ground. Heels should still come just above 90 degrees (the back of the knee)
Medium Pace	5	100m	Jog back	Increase the pace to medium and adjust the technique to match it
Fast Pace	5	100m	Jog/walk back	Increase the pace to a fast pace and adjust the technique to match it
Own pace	4	*4 minutes continuous*		Find your rhythm and adjust your technique and cadence to match your speed

Exercises & Cool-Down: 10-15 Minutes

Activation/Mobility Set 5 + walk or jog

WEEK 6

TECHNIQUE LESSON 6:
Practice

If you have been following the programme and doing the homework, you will find that your running technique has changed and you find it difficult to revert to your old technique. This is the week you run for longer periods of fifteen minutes or more.

You should be able to maintain the new running technique for longer periods and you won't have to think about what to do with your arms and legs. However, this is not the time to stop practicing! Keep going. If you still need more time to improve your fitness or tweak your technique, go back, and review any Lessons or Sessions you feel that you need.

WEEK 6 SCHEDULE

DAY	SESSION DESCRIPTION	DURATION
1	Running Technique Session 6	60 min
2	Walk or Rest + Activation/Mobility (Set 6)	45 min
3	DMS (Set 1) + Strength (Set 1)	45 min
4	Repeat Running Technique Session 6	60 min
5	Walk + Activation/Mobility (Set 6)	30 min
6	DMS (Set 2) + Strength (Set 2)	45 min
7	Repeat Running Technique Session 6	60 min

Technique Session 6

Practice

Warm-Up: 10-15 Minutes

See Warm-Up Section OR Use your own Warm-Up + Activation/Mobility Set 6

SESSION: 45 to 60 Minutes

Speed	Sets	Distance	Recovery Time	Focus
Medium Pace	5	50m	Jog back	Focus on the new technique for the reps then jog back using old technique
Medium Pace	5	200m	Jog/walk back	Leg cycle + arm drive + individual refinements - appropriate to your medium pace
Fast Pace	5	200m	Jog/walk back	Leg cycle + arm drive + individual refinements - appropriate to your fast pace
Medium Pace	4	3 min	1min recovery	Leg cycle + arm drive + individual refinements - appropriate to your medium pace
Medium pace	3	4 min	Jog back	Focus on the technique. Test to see if your technique maintains itself when you are not thinking about it
Run	1	15 min	walk back	Do not focus on the technique. Test to see if your technique maintains itself when you are not thinking about it
Medium Pace	5	50m	Jog back	Focus on the new technique for the reps then jog back using old technique

Exercises & Cool-Down: 10-15 Minutes

Activation/Mobility Set 6 + walk or jog

Weeks 7 & 8

TECHNIQUE LESSON 7 & 8:
Testing the New Technique

By this point you will have been practicing for at least six weeks. Hopefully the new and improved technique is working for you – meaning it has all come together and it feels coordinated and more natural.

Now we begin to focus on making the runs longer while maintaining good technique.

If you feel you still need to make any refinements, go back, and review any Lessons or Sessions you feel that you need.

We are confident that you will have made some amazing progress. And you may well find yourself experiencing more enjoyable runs, less injuries and faster times.

But we know that self-coaching is not easy and not for everyone.

Even though you may not have to consciously focus on your technique at this point, it is still important to keep the coaching cues in mind, and to make some of your weekly runs 'technique runs' where you should focus only on your technique – not distance or speed.

You should still do a 'technique check' frequently, ensure you haven't started to compensate or fall back into old habits when fatigue sets in.

Try to incorporate it at the beginning of your interval running session after the warm-up.

NEW VIDEOS
This would now be a good opportunity to take 'after' videos if you had decided to take 'before' videos. This will allow you to see how you have improved.

WEEK 7 & 8 SCHEDULE

DAY	SESSION DESCRIPTION	DURATION
1	Running Technique Session 7 & 8	60 min
2	DMS (Set 1) + Activation/Mobility (Set 6)	45 min
3	DMS (Set 2) + Strength (Set 1)	45 min
4	Repeat Running Technique Session 7 & 8	60 min
5	Walk + Activation/Mobility (Set 6)	30 min
6	DMS (Set 1) + Strength (Set 2)	45 min
7	Repeat Running Technique Session 7 & 8	60 min

*Note: For Warm-Up, Activation, Mobility, Strength & DMS/Proprioception exercises, refer to the Exercise Library

*Note 2: If you are an advanced runner then you can replace your walk/rest days with your usual run or strength days.

Technique Session7 & 8

Testing the New Technique

Warm-Up: 10-15 Minutes

See Warm-Up Section OR Use your own Warm-Up + Activation/Mobility Set 7

SESSION: 45 to 60 Minutes

Speed	Sets	Distance	Recovery Time	Focus
Medium Pace	10	30 secs	1 min walking	Run at a comfortable pace and focus on technique
Own Pace	1	30 min	n/a	Do not focus on the technique. Test to see if your technique maintains itself when you are not thinking about it, but do a periodic technique check

Exercises & Cool-Down: 10-15 Minutes

Activation/Mobility Set 7 + walk or jog

182

7

EXERCISE LIBRARY

In this section you will see the following:
- Introduction to Exercise Library
- Exercise Sets & Tables
  - Runner's Warm-Up
  - Activation & Mobility
  - DMS / Proprioception
  - Strength
- Exercise Instructions
  - Mobility
  - Activation
  - DMS / Proprioception
  - Strength

INTRODUCTION TO EXERCISE LIBRARY

Runners' Warm-Up

Probably the most common mistake that the many runners make is not warming up, or not warming up well enough before a run. Most runners recognise that it is important to warm up before a run, but don't see it as part of the running process.

Stretching is not warming up!

Doing a few stretches before you run is not warming up. In fact, the evidence shows that stretching before you warm-up, and for longer than 20-30 seconds, reduces the effectiveness and power output of the muscles.

Although most runners have heard that warming up before a run is important, they still don't warm-up correctly or for long enough. The excuses that they give themselves and the therapist when they get injured, are many and varied:

- I don't have time to warm up, too busy
- I did a few stretches isn't that enough?
- I do warm up, I start running slowly and then build up
- If I warm up I will be too tired to run
- Warming up is for wimps
- I sit in the car with the heating on
- I wear extra layers
- I walk for a few minutes

But we think the real reason is that most runners don't know the benefits of a warm-up before a run and what to do to warm-up.

Why Warm Up?

There are several major benefits to warming up.

Physiological benefits: The muscles get ready for exercise. If you have been sitting down all day and suddenly you want to run, and the quads, hamstrings, calves, and hip flexors are tight like a guitar string something may go ping!

You will increase the core temperature of the body. The heart and lungs will be prepared for work.

If you do the correct warm-up and mobility exercises and work through the range of motion, the joints and the tendons will be ready to exercise.

Performance improvement is proven, in both the evidence and the studies, in 80% of elite athletes who warm up sufficiently.

Neural benefits: Warming up readies the nervous system to fire and recruit the muscles. It improves the sensitivity of the nerve receptors and the function of the nervous system.

Doing dynamic exercises gets the proprioceptive system ready to interact with the ground and report back to the brain on any issues.

Mental benefits: Warming up gives us a mental alertness and focus on the objective, getting us ready psychologically to exercise. Our endorphins begin to kick-in quicker. Even when we don't feel like running the movement during the warm-up pushes away the lethargy and changes our mood.

How to Warm Up?

- The process and the sequence of 'HOW' you warm up matters

- The warm-up should last between 15 and 20 minutes depending on fitness levels

- Ideally you should perform warm-up exercises to a point where you are sweating mildly

- The warm-up should include upper body and lower body dynamic exercises to get the muscles, heart and lungs ready to exercise

- If you do any static stretching exercises these should be done at the end of the warm-up routine and last about 5-10 seconds each

- You should not cool down too much after your warm-up and before you start running

Mobility

Most people think that mobility and flexibility are the same thing, when in fact they are two quite different concepts.

Flexibility is stretching a muscle or muscle groups to lengthen passively through a range of motion.

Mobility is the ability of a joint to move actively through a range of motion. Mobility is not only the muscles stretching over a joint but also how far the joint moves within the joint capsule. Mobility also includes the component of motor control within the nervous system.

Mobility training is more effective than traditional 'stretching' because it is based on movement and motor control. Your central nervous system will limit your mobility based on how much control you have. Think of it as lubricating the joins through movement. If you are new to running or run a lot, then you may encounter tightness and lack of mobility in areas like the IT band, the hip, calves, lower back and upper thoracic. The mobility exercises are designed to be used after the warm-up or at the end of your running sessions. You should select the ones that you think will work for you and practice them regularly as part of your running routine.

Muscle Activation

What do we mean by muscle activation? Muscle activation exercises prepare the muscles to fire in the right sequence to improve the efficiency of the movement. This is particularly important for the power muscles - the glutes and the hamstrings - which we use to propel us forward in walking and in running. Using the power muscles correctly, will also help 'share' the load between the muscles and prevent injury. We can do this as a pre-activity and post-activity.

It is especially important that activation exercises are functional to running. Activation exercises will help train the nervous system to fire the right muscles at the right time during a movement. As running is a standing sport and we are only on one leg at any one time, it is important to get the power muscles activated functionally. The preference is to carry out exercises in a standing position (where we can also utilise gravity) rather than lying down.

As with any exercise, technique of the movement is very important. But this is especially true for activation exercises as we're not concerned with pure strength. We are concerned with what muscles are activating in what order. It's important that you don't just go through the motions with these exercises, but that you make each repetition count so that you're reinforcing good movement patterns.

The Dynamic Movement Skills (DMS) activation exercises can also be used as part of the warm-up and some of the exercises are included in the warm-up routines. These also incorporate proprioception and single leg exercises designed to help with balance and the interaction with the ground. Please ensure you warm up well before the DMS exercises.

Strength

Strength training will improve your performance and prevent injuries. It is an essential complement to a runner's training because it strengthens muscles and joints, which can decrease injury risk. It also helps with better mobility. If you want to run at your full potential, you need to take a thorough approach to running. We have reviewed the benefits of dynamic movement and plyometrics plus the benefits you get to your running economy and speed in the Proprioception and Dynamic Movement Skills chapter.

Running requires a solid foundation, and strength in the core and the arms are equally important to the legs. When you run, your abdominal and back muscles can help you to stabilise your posture and stop you from leaning forward. Strengthening your core is important, and we don't just mean the abdominal muscles. We mean, glutes, hips, hip-flexors, abdominal and back lower back muscles. Arm movement is important to good running technique and the kinetic chain, so you need to work on your upper body as well.

EXERCISE SETS
& TABLES

In this section you will see the suggested exercises and sets mentioned in your weekly schedules in the Running Re-Education section. For a description of how to do each exercise, please refer to the next section in this chapter. All exercises and sets are numbered for easier navigation.

RUNNER'S WARM-UP

OPTION 1 - Dynamic Warm-Up (15-20 minutes)

1. **Straight ahead jogging** for 40 metres

2. **Arms Swings forward with Skip** – Skip straight ahead with arms moving around and forward from the shoulders -30 seconds/metres

3. **Arms Swing Backwards with Skip** – Skip straight ahead with arms moving around and backwards from the shoulders -30 seconds/metres

4. **Straight ahead jogging** for 40 metres

5. **Wide chest extension with Skip-** Skip straight ahead with arms wide moving backwards and forward from the shoulders -30 seconds/metres

6. **Straight ahead jogging** for 40 metres

7. **Arms swing side to side with Skip-** Skip straight ahead with arms stretched out moving together to the left and right of the torso in the skipping rhythm (left-right-left right) from the shoulders -30 seconds/metres

8. **Straight ahead jogging** for 40 metres

9. **High Knees** - perform knees-up on the spot. Knees raise to 90 degrees, arms pumping at the side. 10 seconds Repeat 4 times.

10. **Torso Twists** - torso twists on the spot. Arms loose moving side to side with the rhythm. 15 seconds Repeat 4 times.

11. **Straight ahead jogging** for 40 metres

12. **Butt Kicks** - butt kicks while running. Ankles touching the butt, arms pumping at the side. 15 seconds Repeat 4 times

13. **Straight ahead jogging** for 40 metres

14. **Knee across the body** - Straight ahead skipping, alternatively the right knee comes across the body then lands and then the left knee comes across and then lands. 20 seconds

15. **Sideways Quick Steps** - Quick short side steps without crossing over the legs. Left then right 20 seconds, repeat twice

16. **Straight ahead jogging** for 40 metres

17. **Do any individual mobility or stretching exercises that you normally do.**

18. Let's Run!

OPTION 2 – Walk-Run Warm-Up (15-20 minutes)

1. Walk for 6 minutes with medium to fast walk
2. Swing, both arms like a windmill forward gently 10 times and backwards 10 times while you are still walking. Repeat 3 times
3. While walking, open your arms wide 10 times and bring them together at chest height, repeat 3 times
4. While walking Swing both arms to the left 10 times and to the right 10 times and repeat
5. Standing and if you wish holding on to a wall or tree: Swing your knee up and back ten times, repeat with the other leg
6. Walk briskly for 2 minutes
7. Run for 20 metres – Walk for 20 metres - Repeat 5 times
8. Let's start running!

OPTION 3 – Dynamic Warm-Up 2 (15-20minutes)

1. Dynamic Movement Skills – Quick feet
   a. Leading with the left foot 20 secs Forward REST 10 secs
   b. Leading with the right foot 20 secs Forward REST 10 secs
   c. Leading with the left foot 20 secs Backwards REST 10 secs
   d. Leading with the right foot 20 secs Backwards REST 10 secs
   e. REPEAT SEQUENCE
2. Jog for 1 minute. Then while walking:
   a. Swing, both arms like a windmill forward gently 10 times and backwards 10 times while you are still walking or jogging. Repeat 3 times.
3. While walking or jogging open your arms wide 10 times and bring them together at chest height, repeat 3 times.
4. Jog for 2 minutes. Then Walk
5. While walking or jogging swing both arms to the left 10 times and to the right 10 times and repeat.
6. Jog for 2 minutes
7. Dynamic Movement – Quick feet
   a. Leading with the left foot 20 secs Forward REST 10 secs
   b. Leading with the right foot 20 secs Forward REST 10 secs
   c. Leading with the left foot 20 secs Backwards REST 10 secs
   d. Leading with the right foot 20 secs Backwards REST 10 secs
8. Let's start running!

ACTIVATION & MOBILITY

SET 1

MOBILITY		
Exercise	**Sets**	**Reps**
1. Hip Bends	2 Sets	10
2. Long Lever Hip Flexor Release	2 Sets on Each Leg	10
ACTIVATION		
Exercise	**Sets**	**Reps**
9. Anterior Step & Reach	2 Sets on Each Leg	10
10. Diagonal Glute Kicks	1 Set on Each Leg	15

SET 2

MOBILITY		
Exercise	**Sets**	**Reps**
2. Long Lever Hip Flexor Release	2 Sets on Each Leg	10
3. Short Lever Hip Flexor Release	2 Sets on Each Leg	10
ACTIVATION		
Exercise	**Sets**	**Reps**
9. Anterior Step & Reach	3 Sets on Each Leg	10
11. Sideways Walking with Bands	3 Walks Each side	10
12. Functional Core Rotations	2 Sets	30

SET 3

MOBILITY		
Exercise	**Sets**	**Reps**
5. Half Step Matrix	2 Sets on Each Leg	5
6. Heel Tap Walks	4 Sets of walks	15
3. Short Lever Hip Flexor Release	2 Set on Each Leg	10
ACTIVATION		
Exercise	**Sets**	**Reps**
13. Loaded Anterior Step & Rotate	2 Sets on Each Leg	10
14. Dynamic Step	4 Sets on Each Leg	5
18. Footwork - Forward	2 Sets on Each Leg	20 secs.
19. Footwork - Backward	2 Sets on Each Leg	20 secs.

SET 4

MOBILITY		
Exercise	**Sets**	**Reps**
3. Short Lever Hip Flexor Release	2 Sets on Each Leg	10
5. Half Step Matrix	1 Set on Each Leg	5
7. Foot Mobility	4 Sets on Each Leg	10
ACTIVATION		
Exercise	**Sets**	**Reps**
13. Loaded Anterior Step & Rotate	2 Sets on Each Leg	10
14. Dynamic Step	4 Sets on Each Leg	5
15. Back & Diagonal Steps w/Bands	5 Sets on Each Leg	10

SET 5

MOBILITY		
Exercise	**Sets**	**Reps**
5. Half Step Matrix	1 Set on Each Leg	5
4. Long Lever Hip Flexor Release with Rotation	2 Sets on Each Leg	10
8. Backwards Walking with Bands	5 Sets	6 Steps
ACTIVATION		
Exercise	**Sets**	**Reps**
15. Single Leg 3-Way Reach	3 Sets on Each Leg	3
21. Single Leg Jumps - Backward	2 Sets on Each Leg	10 secs.
16. Single Leg 90° Hop and Holds	2 Sets on Each Leg	10

SET 6

MOBILITY		
Exercise	**Sets**	**Reps**
3. Short Lever Hip Flexor Release	2 Sets on Each Leg	10
6. Heel Tap Walks	4 Sets of walks	15
4. Long Lever Hip Flexor Release with Rotation	2 Sets on Each Leg	10
ACTIVATION		
Exercise	**Sets**	**Reps**
9. Anterior Step & Reach	3 Sets on Each Leg	10
25. Single Leg Jumps - Lateral	2 Sets on Each Leg	10 secs.
16. Single Leg 90° Hop and Holds	2 Sets on Each Leg	10

SET 7

MOBILITY		
Exercise	**Sets**	**Reps**
4. Long Lever Hip Flexor Release with Rotation	2 Sets on Each Leg	10
7. Foot Mobility	4 Sets on Each Leg	10
8. Backwards Walking with Bands	5 Sets of walks	6 Steps
ACTIVATION		
Exercise	**Sets**	**Reps**
24. Single Leg Jumps - Backward	2 Sets on Each Leg	10 secs.
25. Single Leg Jumps - Lateral	2 Sets on Each Leg	10 secs.
16. Single Leg 90° Hop and Holds	2 Sets on Each Leg	10

DMS / PROPRIOCEPTION

SET 1

FOOTWORK		
*Recovery should be **20 seconds** between sets		
Exercise	**Sets**	**Time**
18. Footwork - Forward - Left Leg Lead	1	20 secs.
Footwork - Forward - Right Leg Lead	1	20 secs.
19. Footwork - Backward - Left Leg Lead	1	20 secs.
Footwork - Backward - Right Leg Lead	1	20 secs.
REPEAT THE ABOVE SET 2 TIMES		**5-6 mins.**
DOUBLE LEG JUMPS		
*Recovery should be **30 seconds** between sets		
Exercise	**Sets**	**Reps**
20. Double Leg Jumps Forward	1	20 secs.
21. Double Leg Jumps Backward	1	20 secs.
22. Double Leg Jumps - Lateral - Left	1	20 secs.
Double Leg Jumps - Lateral - Right	1	20 secs.
		2-3 mins.
SINGLE LEG JUMPS		
*Recovery should be **20 seconds** between sets		
Exercise	**Sets**	**Time**
23. Single Leg Jumps Forward - Left Leg	1	10 secs.
Single Leg Jumps Forward - Right Leg	1	10 secs.
24. Single Leg Jumps Backward - Left Leg	1	10 secs.
Single Leg Jumps Backward - Right Leg	1	10 secs.
25. Single Leg Jumps Lateral - Left Leg	1	10 secs.
Single Leg Jumps Lateral - Right Leg	1	10 secs.
		3 mins.

SET 2

FOOTWORK *Recovery should be **20 seconds** between sets		
Exercise	**Sets**	**Time**
18. Footwork - Forward - Left Leg Lead	1	20 secs.
Footwork - Forward - Right Leg Lead	1	20 secs.
19. Footwork - Backward - Left Leg Lead	1	20 secs.
Footwork - Backward - Right Leg Lead	1	20 secs.
REPEAT THE ABOVE SET 2 TIMES		**5-6 mins.**
DOUBLE LEG JUMPS *Recovery should be **30 seconds** between sets		
Exercise	**Sets**	**Reps**
20. Double Leg Jumps Forward	1	20 secs.
21. Double Leg Jumps Backward	1	20 secs.
22. Double Leg Jumps - Lateral - Left	1	20 secs.
Double Leg Jumps - Lateral - Right	1	20 secs.
		2-3 mins.

STRENGTH

SET 1

STRENGTH		
Exercise	**Sets**	**Reps**
29. Slow Air Squats	3 Sets	10
26. Step-ups on Box	3 Sets on each leg	10
27. Sumo Squats	3 Sets	10
30. Running Arms with Weights	3 Sets	20 secs.
26. Step-ups on Box	3 Sets on each leg	15
28. Single Leg Pendulum	3 Sets on each leg	5
27. Sumo Squat	3 Sets	10
30. Running Arms with Weights	3 Sets	20 secs.
31. Planks on Swiss Ball	4 Sets	20 secs.

SET 2

STRENGTH		
Exercise	**Sets**	**Reps**
26. Step-ups on Box	3 Sets on each leg	10
32. Single Leg Assisted Squats	3 Sets on each leg	10
33. Split Squats on Box	4 Sets on each leg	5
34. Double leg Jumps on Box	5 Sets	10
33. Split Squats on Box	4 Sets on each leg	5
28. Single Leg Pendulum	3 Sets on each leg	5
31. Planks on Swiss ball	4 Sets	20 secs.

EXERCISE INSTRUCTIONS

This section is a description of how to perform all exercises with correct technique. Please note that many exercises can cross over in terms of purpose. For example, some will achieve both activation and proprioceptive training. Others will achieve mobility and activation, etc. We have tried to categorise them according to their main function and for easy navigation.

MOBILITY

1. Hip Bends

INSTRUCTIONS

1. Stand with feet hip-width apart
2. Keep knees unlocked and slowly bend from the hips
3. Bring your torso parallel to the ground with your neck in line
4. As far as you are able to go until you feel your hamstrings
5. Reverse the movement to return to standing and repeat

TIPS

- Keep a flat back and ensure the bend comes from the hips and not the lower back
- Ensure knees and feet are facing forward

2. Long Lever Hip Flexor Release

INSTRUCTIONS

1. Stand on right leg keeping the knee straight. Place the left foot on a box/step
2. While keeping the pelvis in a neutral position, ease forward so that the left hip goes into extension. Keep the back foot flat on the ground
3. Feet and hips point forward
4. Hold for a count of 5-6 seconds. Ease back out
5. Repeat the exercise sequence on the opposite leg

TIPS

- Ensure the pelvis stays neutral and you don't arch your back
- Ensure the hips stay facing forwards

3. Short Lever Hip Flexor Release

INSTRUCTIONS

1. Kneel on left knee keeping the left foot in a dorsiflexed position. Place the right foot on the ground, so the knee is at 90 degrees
2. While keeping the pelvis in a neutral position, ease forward so that the left hip goes into extension
3. Hold for a count of 5-6 seconds then ease back out
4. Repeat the exercise sequence on the same leg 5-10 times
5. Repeat on the opposite leg

TIPS

- Ensure the pelvis stays neutral and you don't arch your back
- Ensure the hips stay facing forwards

4. Long Lever Hip Flexor Release with Rotation

INSTRUCTIONS

1. Stand on left leg keeping the knee straight. Place the right foot on a box/step
2. While keeping the pelvis in a neutral position, ease forward so that the right hip goes into extension. Keep the back foot flat on the ground
3. With arms extended and palms facing upwards, rotate over the bent leg
4. Hold for a count of 5-6 seconds. Ease back out
5. Repeat 5-10 times on the same leg
6. Repeat the exercise sequence on the opposite leg

TIPS

- Ensure the pelvis stays neutral and you don't arch your back
- Ensure the hips and the feet stay facing forwards

5. Half Step Matrix

INSTRUCTIONS

1. Stand in a neutral position. Extend your arms and place palms to-gether
2. Step forward and diagonally across your midline and transfer your full weight onto stepping leg
3. Keep both feet flat on the ground
4. Hold for a count of 3-4 seconds
5. Rotate to the left and hold for a count of 2 seconds.
6. Rotate to the right and hold for a count of 2 seconds
7. Repeat the exercise sequence 5 times
8. Repeat the exercise on the opposite leg

TIPS

- Keep the non-stepping foot flat on the ground (i.e. don't let the heel lift)
- Try to keep hips facing forward
- Try to keep the feet flat and facing forwards

6. Heel Tap Walks

INSTRUCTIONS

1. Keeping an upright back, lift (flick) one foot to the front of the body as if to see the sole of your shoe. When the ankle is in touching distance, lightly tap it and let the foot return to the floor under control
2. Repeat the same process continuously alternating sides and walking forward
3. Walk forward for 10 steps

TIPS

- Try not to bend down from your back

7. Foot Mobility

INSTRUCTIONS

1. Place a resistance band over feet and stand in a neutral position hip width apart with some tension on the band
2. While keeping the heel planted on the ground, rotate one foot outwards at the ankle joint
3. Return to neutral and repeat the process with the same foot for 10-15 repetitions
4. Repeat with the opposite foot

TIPS

- To increase resistance, start by standing with feet further apart
- For better mobility try the same movements without any shoes
- Ensure the feet are facing forward

8. Backwards Walking with Bands

INSTRUCTIONS

1. Place resistance bands around upper leg and lower leg
2. From a ¼ squat position, take a step backwards reaching back with the toes first
3. Walk for a few steps then turn and walk back

TIPS

- Knees should always be in a ¼ squat position
- Use opposite arm and leg to keep your balance
- Try not to lean forward

ACTIVATION

9. Anterior Step & Reach

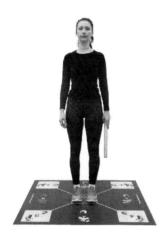

INSTRUCTIONS

1. Step heel-to-toe with right foot forward and diagonally
2. Transfer weight onto right leg keeping a soft knee (slightly bent.
3. Bend from the hips while keeping a flat back
4. Keep the foot planted flat
5. Reach forward with left arm and hold for 2-3 seconds
6. Return to start position & repeat
7. Repeat the exercise sequence on the same leg 10 times
8. Repeat the exercise sequence on the opposite leg

TIPS

- Keep the foot pointing forward
- Hold until you feel the glute working

211

10. Diagonal Glute Kicks

INSTRUCTIONS

1. Make a 'tabletop' with your back
2. From a flexed hip position, extend leg to the backward keeping the foot and leg externally rotated
3. Try to keep controlled through the back and pelvis but reach high enough so you feel the glute and hamstring working
4. Hold for a count of 2 and repeat on the same leg
5. Repeat on the opposite side

TIPS

- Don't arch your back to gain more leg height
- Move slowly
- Keep the standing leg straight

11. Sideways Walking with Bands

INSTRUCTIONS

1. Place resistance bands around upper and lower leg
2. Stand in a ¼ squat position
3. Step sideways with the left leg
4. Bring the right leg to meet the left in a controlled manner repeat across ten steps
5. Repeat the exercise sequence on the opposite leg

TIPS

- Stay in a ¼ position throughout the exercise
- Keep feet facing forward and flat

12. Functional Core Rotations

INSTRUCTIONS

1. Stand with feet hip width apart with soft knees and hold a swiss ball with long arms, below chest height
2. Keeping the hips facing forward, rotate the ball to the left and to the right continuously
3. Keep the head and upper body steady and facing forward

TIPS

- Ensure power and movement is generated by the core and not the arms

13. Loaded Anterior Step & Rotate

INSTRUCTIONS

1. Stand with feet parallel holding swiss ball. With your left foot, take a diagonal step forward, stepping heel-to-toe and transferring weight onto the stepping leg. Allow the heel of the non- stepping foot to come off the ground to ensure full weight transfer
2. Rotate through the pelvis over the stepping leg. Allow the movement to continue to a natural end point by rotating through spine
3. Return to start position and repeat
4. Repeat the exercise sequence on the opposite leg

TIPS

- Ensure weight is mostly on the stepping/front leg
- Keep weight going through the heel of the stepping leg
- Keep the foot flat on the ground and facing straight
- Don't force the rotation

14. Dynamic Step

INSTRUCTIONS

1. Start by standing on left leg with a soft knee
2. With the right foot, take a long, dynamic step / hop forward and land heel-toe - with a soft knee. Find your balance and hold for a count of 2
3. With the right foot, take a large dynamic step backward and land forefoot and heel back to your starting point - with a soft knee Find your balance and hold for a count of 2 and repeat 5 times
4. Repeat the exercise sequence on the opposite leg

TIPS

- When landing, don't allow the knee to bend to a point that is past your toes. Keep the knee aligned over the foot
- Don't stay on your toes when balancing keep the foot flat on the ground
- Ensure knee does not collapse inwards

15. Single Leg 3 Way Reach (with stick)

INSTRUCTIONS

1. Stand on left leg with a soft knee
2. Hold a small baton/rolling pin <u>OR</u> place palms together with arms straight
3. Bending from the hip (and not from the back) tip forward and to the left to reach across the body. Return to starting position without putting the right leg on the ground

4. Bending from the hip (and not from the back) tip forward reach directly forward. Return to starting position without putting the right leg on the ground
5. Bending from the hip (and not from the back) tip forward and to the right to reach across the body. Return to starting position without putting the right leg on the ground
6. Repeat 3 times on the same leg
7. Repeat the exercise sequence on the opposite leg

TIPS

• Can be done with palms together and straight arms

16. Single Leg 90° Hop & Hold

INSTRUCTIONS

1. Stand on left leg to the left of a line
2. With left leg, hop and rotate 90 degrees to the right, crossing the line. Landing should be midfoot. Hold for a count of 2 sec
3. Hop back across the line turning 90 degrees to the left landing. Hold for a count of 2
4. Repeat 10 times
5. Repeat the exercise sequence on the opposite leg

TIPS

- Ensure your heel comes down and the foot is flat after every hop

17. Back & Diagonal Steps with Bands

INSTRUCTIONS

1. Place resistance bands around upper leg and lower leg
2. Stand with both legs hip width apart
3. Step backwards and diagonally with the right foot keeping the weight through the left leg
4. Repeat 10 times
5. Repeat the exercise sequence on the opposite leg

TIPS

- Keep the weight on the standing leg

DMS / PROPRIOCEPTION

---

18. Footwork - Forward

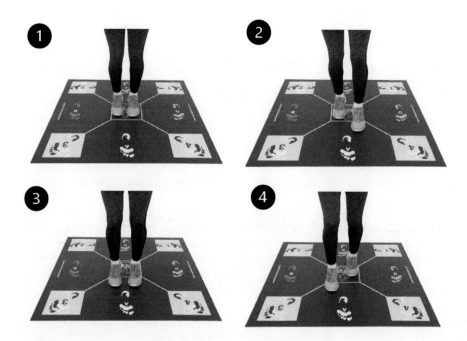

INSTRUCTIONS

1. Stand behind a line on the ground
2. Take a small step forward across the line with the left foot
3. Bring right foot to meet left foot
4. Step backwards with left foot across the line
5. Bring right foot to meet left foot
6. Repeat continuously for 20 seconds

TIPS

- Keep weight through balls of the feet
- Move feet across the line in rhythm
- Start off slowly and move as fast as you can but within your comfort and control
- Arms should stay relaxed and head up not down

19. Footwork - Backward

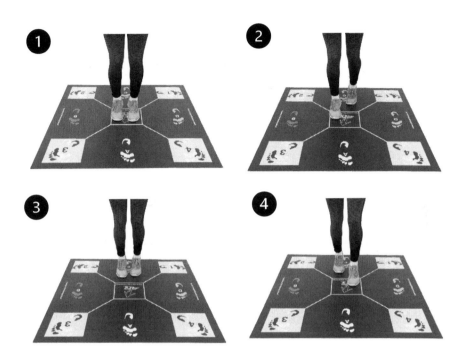

INSTRUCTIONS

1. Stand in front of a line on the ground
2. Take a small step back across the line with the left foot
3. Bring right foot to meet left foot
4. Step forward with left foot across the line
5. Bring right foot to meet left foot
6. Repeat continuously for 20 seconds

TIPS

- Keep weight through balls of the feet
- Move feet across the line in rhythm
- Start off slowly and move as fast as you can but within your comfort and control
- Arms should stay relaxed and head up not down

20. Double Leg Jumps – Forward

INSTRUCTIONS

1. Stand behind a line
2. Hop forwards across the line
3. Immediately hop backwards across line
4. Repeat continuously for 20 seconds

TIPS

- Move as quickly as possible as the aim is to minimise the time the foot touches the ground
- Keep weight through balls of the feet
- Start off slowly and move as fast as you can but within your comfort zone
- Arms should stay relaxed

21. Double Leg Jumps – Backward

INSTRUCTIONS

1. Stand on both legs in front of a line
2. Hop backwards across the line
3. Immediately hop forwards across line
4. Repeat continuously for 20 seconds

TIPS

- Move as quickly as possible as the aim is to minimise the time the foot touches the ground
- Feet pointing straight
- Keep weight through balls of the feet
- Start off slowly and move as fast as you can but within your comfort zone
- Arms should stay relaxed

22. Double Leg Jumps – Lateral

INSTRUCTIONS

1. Stand to the left of a line
2. Hop sideways using both legs (to the right) across the line landing
3. Immediately hop back over the line (to the left)
4. Repeat continuously for 20 seconds

TIPS

- Keep weight through balls of the feet
- Feet pointing straight
- Start off slowly and move as fast as you can but within your comfort zone
- Arms should stay relaxed

23. Single Leg Jumps – Forward

INSTRUCTIONS

1. Stand on left leg behind a line
2. With left leg, hop forwards across the line
3. Immediately hop backwards across line
4. Repeat continuously for 10 seconds
5. Repeat the exercise sequence on the opposite leg

TIPS

- Move as quickly as possible as the aim is to minimise the time the foot touches the ground
- Keep weight through balls of the feet
- Start off slowly and move as fast as you can but within your comfort zone
- Arms should stay relaxed

24. Single Leg Jumps – Backward

INSTRUCTIONS

1. Stand on left leg in front of a line
2. With left leg, hop backwards across the line
3. Immediately hop forwards across line
4. Repeat continuously for 10 seconds
5. Repeat the exercise sequence on the opposite leg

TIPS

- Move as quickly as possible as the aim is to minimise the time the foot touches the ground
- Keep weight through balls of the feet
- Start off slowly and move as fast as you can but within your comfort zone
- Arms should stay relaxed

25. Single Leg Jumps – Lateral

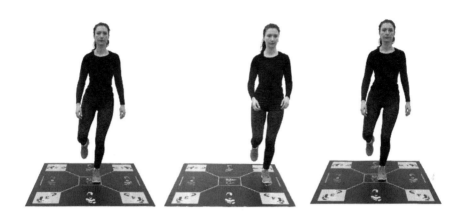

INSTRUCTIONS

1. Stand on left leg to the right of a line
2. With left leg, hop sideways (to the left) across the line landing on ball of the foot
3. Immediately hop back over the line (to the right)
4. Repeat continuously for 10 seconds
5. Repeat the exercise sequence on the opposite leg

TIPS

- Keep weight through balls of the feet
- Start off slowly and move as fast as you can but within your comfort and control
- Arms should stay relaxed

STRENGTH

---

26. Step-Ups on Box

INSTRUCTIONS

1. Stand in front of step holding weights
2. Place the left foot flat onto the box
3. Keeping your weight through the left heel, step up onto the box
4. Step down with the right foot in a controlled manner, keeping the weight through the right heel
5. Repeat 10 -15 times
6. Repeat the exercise sequence on the opposite leg

TIPS

- Box height 10-12 inches - No higher than a foot
- Weight guidance: Depending on strength, use a weight between 5kg & 20kg
- Body upright
- Ensure the whole foot is on the box
- Knee should stay aligned over the foot/toes – not ahead of toes
- Keep feet straight

27. Sumo Squat

SIDE VIEW

INSTRUCTIONS

1. Stand with feet parallel and wider than shoulder-width apart – holding a weight with both hands
2. Keeping the weight through the heels, bend the legs into a squat position
3. Pushing the hips back like sitting into a chair
4. Push through the heels to return slowly to a standing position

TIPS

- Weight guidance: Use a weight between 5kg and 15 kg
- Knee should stay aligned over the foot/toes – not ahead of toe
- Feet pointing straight ahead
- Aim for a 90 bend in the knees
- Don't bend forward from the waist

28. Single Leg pendulum

INSTRUCTIONS

1. Stand with feet next to each other, holding a weight in both hands
2. Balance on one leg keeping the knee soft (slightly bend)
3. Slowly lower the weight towards the ground whilst keeping it close to the supporting leg and allow the non-supporting to rise to counterbalance
4. Once you reach a low enough point where you can still balance, reverse the movement to return to a starting position
5. Repeat 5 times
6. Repeat the exercise sequence on the opposite leg

TIPS

- Weight Guidance: Depending on strength, aim to use a 5kg weight
- Keep the weight through the heel of the supporting leg to help activate the glutes
- Keep the foot flat on the box

29. Slow Air Squats

SIDE VIEW

INSTRUCTIONS

1. Stand with feet parallel and shoulder-width apart
2. Keeping the weight through the heels, bend the legs into a squat position raising the arms to above shoulder height
3. Push through the heels to return slowly to a standing position and lower the arms

TIPS

- Keep the weight through both feet
- Keep the feet and knees pointing forward

30. Running Arms with Weights

INSTRUCTIONS

1. Stand with left foot forward. Plant your weight through the front foot
2. Back foot balanced on the ball of the foot
3. Hold dumbbells (or alternative weight) in arms with elbows bend at 90 degrees or less
4. Mimicking a running arm drive, drive the arms backward and forwards using good arm technique for 10 seconds
5. Bring the hands to shoulder height
6. Repeat the exercise sequence on the opposite leg

TIPS

- Weigh Guidance: Use light weights i.e., 2-3 kg

31. Plank on Swiss Ball

INSTRUCTIONS

1. Using a fitness ball, get into a plank position with elbows resting on top of the ball
2. Slowly roll the ball forwards a few inches using your elbows
3. Return to starting position in a controlled manner
4. Repeat 15 times
5. Using a fitness ball, get into a plank position with elbows resting on top of the ball
6. Slowly roll the ball forwards a few inches using your elbows
7. Return to starting position in a controlled manner
8. Repeat 15 times

TIPS

- Don't let hips sink in order to not stress your back
- To modify this movement and make it easier, do a plank position from the knees

32. Single Leg Assisted Squats

SIDE VIEW

INSTRUCTIONS

1. Stand on the right leg beside a wall or chair for support. Hold a weight in the right hand
2. In a controlled manner
3. Lower yourself into a 1/4 squat position, keeping the weight through the heel.
4. Hold for 3 secs and return to standing position
5. Repeat 10 times on the same leg
6. Change to the opposite leg

TIPS

- Knee should stay aligned over the foot/toes – not ahead of toes
- Ensure knee does not collapse inwards
- Weight through the heel with the foot flat

33. Split Squats on Box

INSTRUCTIONS

1. Stand in lunge position with left leg on a step/box, holding weights in each hand
2. Keeping the weight through the left heel, with the foot flat, lower yourself into a lunge position
3. Slowly return to starting position
4. Repeat 5 times
5. Repeat on the opposite leg

TIPS

- Box height 6 inches
- Keep the knee over the foot, and not the toes, so as not to put extra pressure on the knee
- Only bend to 90 degrees
- Weight Guidance: between 5-7kg

34. Double Leg Jumps on Box

INSTRUCTIONS

1. These are continuous jumps onto the box landing on the balls of the feet
2. Then drop back down onto the floor again landing on the balls of the feet
3. Repeat for 10 jumps

TIPS

- Be light on your feet
- Jump and return
- Use your arms to give you elevation
- Box height 10-12 inches

ABOUT THE AUTHOR

Mike Antoniades

Mike is the founder and Performance & Rehabilitation Director of The Movement School ® & The Running School ®.

He has been a coach for over forty years and has specialised in speed for athletes of all sports and movement re-patterning and rehabilitation after injury or surgery.

His clients include among others: athletes and teams from The English Premiership, English Championship, German Bundesliga, Rugby Union, Rugby League, Handball, Lacrosse, European Olympic Associations as well as Elite Track & Field athletes including World & Olympic Gold Medallists.

Mike developed the Dynamic Movement Skills® (DMS) Methodology, which is being used in over 2000 organisations, including physical therapy practices, schools, and professional sports clubs.

Mike is the co-author of two books on **'Youth Fitness' and '101 Fitness Drills for 7-11 & 12-16 years'.** He is also the author of the DVD on developing speed in football called **'Feel the Speed'**.

Mike regularly presents at conferences and workshops. He has been featured on TV in the UK, Europe and in the USA and in a number of publications for his work with kids' movement, running and elite athletes.

RESOURCES & EDUCATION COURSES

Locations

For locations and contact details of Certified Movement and Running School Centres and Certified Running Technique Specialists, visit: www.runningschool.com

CPD and Certification Courses

For information on Certification and Education Courses, visit:

Offline courses: www.runningschool.com
Online courses: www.myrunningschool.com